AND THE BAND PLAYED ON

To the memory of
my father and mother

The Friar's Bush Press
24 College Park Ave
Belfast BT7 1LR
1990

Printed by W & G Baird, Antrim

Front cover painted by Barbara Allen

AND THE BAND PLAYED ON

Sketches of Ulster life

by
Gerald Rafferty

Friar's Bush Press

Contents

WHEN WE WERE YOUNG

The demon marble player

In a wee shop window the other day my eye caught sight of a packet of lovely big 'glassy' marbles. Not for a long time had I seen such big 'glassies,' and my memory went back to the times when as a lad, 'shooting marbles' (or 'marvels') along the roads, was a popular sport with young and not so young.

There used to be so many marble holes throughout the land that the local councils were forever sending squads of workmen out to fill them in! Coming home from school from the middle of March onwards, your mother never required an explanation for being an hour or so late. She knew just as sure as the daffodils appeared, the marble games got started. A couple of lads living out the road, would fashion a 'hole' or 'den' or 'well' and the game would get underway. It was a tough job fashioning the 'hole' because you were liable to strike, hard, unrelenting rock. Many a good penknife was destroyed at the job.

So on the way from school, down the Loughgall Road, maybe half a dozen 'holes' were dug. Peter and I always played for marbles as the prize and many a time I went home singing, my pockets full of Peter's highly-prized marbles. And on many an occasion it was vice-versa.

A boy becomes very attached to certain marbles. The odd one was looked upon as lucky and you couldn't have lost a game if you chanced to possess a lucky marble. The stony marble was the king of the marbles. Played with skill they could have smashed a score of big glassies or chalkies. The chalkie was no use for a hard strike but ideal for the dribbler and a dribbler won many a hard fought game.

Bill the Demon Marble Player must have smashed more glassies and chalkies than anyone else in the country. He used a small, half-blackened stony for a strike and one shot was always enough to put paid to an opponent. For the rest of the game, dribbling and 'getting home,' he used an ordinary marble, a chalkie, but never a glassie, which he scorned. Bill the Demon could launch his vicious stony attack either along the ground, or from a raised position. Demon Bill's home ground was under the stone railway bridge, a cold and forbidding place, even on a summer evening, for there was a constant drip of water from the strong and stony edifice. He said once that he fashioned his deadly stony marble from a hunk of the stone bridge but it remained a wonder how he got it shaped so smoothly.

Bill used that little stony for ages and it was the envy of every marble player on the road, from the Mill Row Corner down to Scott's Corner and beyond. One day he allowed the rest of us players to have a shot with his stony but it wouldn't do its deadly work for any of us, so it went to prove that it took the combination of Demon Bill's skill and the stony to do the job. There appeared to be a strong bond between man and marble. There were others who could clear off marbles like Hurricane Higgins on a snooker table, but Alex or Dennis Taylor never had the striking power with the cue and white ball as Demon Bill had with the little stony.

When the last war broke out Demon Bill the Marble Player went off and fought in the army and I didn't hear of him for years. At the war's end he came home for a while and I met him one day and asked him if he still had his famous stony marble. He assured me that it was still safe and sound and that he wouldn't part with it for anything. He told me he once played a game with another soldier at Alamein – and won. It must have been difficult to play marbles in the sandy desert, I suggested. 'Not at all,' said Demon Bill. 'With that wee stony you could play on the top of Mount Everest.' And what did he think of the 'glassies?' He waved me away. 'Don't let my wee stony hear you talk about glassies!'

I wouldn't wonder but Demon Bill still carries that wee stony around with him to this day – as a relic of past victories under the railway bridge and along the Loughgall Road many years ago.

King of the Armagh bullet throwers

As a lad in the thirties my sporting heroes weren't footballers, cricketers or what-have-you, nor was there such a word as 'superstar' in the dictionary. My hero was a fine strapping fellow called Bill George who was the champion bullet-thrower along the roads of Armagh. Now called road bowls and played only in Armagh and Cork, this sport has been very popular around the primatial city for over three hundred years and was first called as far as I know, long bowls, having been introduced to the north by the English.

The 'bullet' is a metal ball about the size of an average orange and weighs 1¾ lbs or 28 ounces and the idea of the game is to see who can cover a pre-arranged distance, usually around three miles, in the least number of throws or shots as they're called. Played mostly on a Sunday, although fifty years ago it was common to see a large crowd assembled on summer evenings throughout the week, the sport still has a big following but these times it is played on the smaller by-roads on account of increased traffic and the fact that most modern highways are too wide and not made for throwing the bullet.

From I was about eight years old I was always out on the roads on summer evenings and often acted as 'marker': a handful of grass was placed on the spot where the metal missile stopped. The game calls for a lot of skill and stamina. A handful of grass also marks the starting point and stripped to shirt and trousers, the thrower takes a short swift race, hops deftly on the right foot (left if you're left-handed) and with a piston-like thrust of the arm, slings the bullet down the road, zooming along at fifty or sixty miles to the hour, so if you're a spectator you need to be nifty in getting out of its path or you could end up with a broken ankle. But the

men who followed the bullet could always easily side-
step it just like a matador dodging a raging bull. A scout
is always posted ahead of the game to give warning of
approaching traffic and I have seen a woman with a pram
holding up a game for ten or fifteen minutes.

'Hammerman' Donnelly was the Armagh champ just
before my time and his amazing skill is still talked of
along the roads, as the man who humbled the mighty
Tim Delaney, the legendary champion from Co. Cork in
a battle royal on the Moy Road fifty or more years ago.

In the hazy summer evenings of the late thirties and
into the forties the Mill Row men threw tuppenny scores
(as the matches were called) down the Loughgall Road
the length of Scott's Corner. Then one day a tall young
farmer from the wilds of Cabragh near the Callan River
walked onto the Loughgall Road and showed them just
how to throw the bullet – and so a star was born, a
man whose name was to become a household word
around Armagh and along the banks of the lovely Lee in
Cork. Bill George was the successor to the 'Hammerman'
Donnelly and went on to beat the best in Cork and thus
become the champion of all-Ireland. I remember vividly
the evening he delivered a shot from Reilly's Rocks, and
'opened' the corner at Ross's blacksmith forge on the
Loughgall Road, a distance of almost a mile. A good
bullet thrower is like a good golfer. He knows every rise
and fall on the road and when he does deliver his shot he
knows exactly where it is going to run its course. With
such as Bill George this seemed to be an inborn talent,
but he was much happier and relaxed when throwing in
the 'tanner' scores than a big match when there was a
book of perhaps £500 in bets on him.

As a lad I used to deem it a high honour to hold
champion Bill's coat while he threw his shots and in
addition he was a neighbour of ours and called often at
the house. And I would like it to go on record that on one
historic occasion for me – a fine June evening it was – I

partnered Bill in a tuppenny score down the road. At that time the game was illegal and the throwers scattered if a policeman was sighted approaching on his bicycle. The bullet was often confiscated and there were occasions when participants had to appear at the local Petty Sessions and were fined half-a-crown. They said there were hundreds of confiscated bullets in Russell Street police barracks, Armagh and as many in Irish Street barracks. But most policemen turned a blind eye to the sport and some were even known to have placed a few bob of a bet on their fancied thrower in a big match.

There were other excellent bullet-throwers around Armagh in the thirties and forties: men like Paddy Lyttle, Jimmy 'Toots' Macklin, Kirk Mallon, Andy Mallon, and my own brother Barney who was a left-handed thrower with much style. Bill George and Barney were close friends and often went to the last house of the movies in the Cosy Corner Picture House. The Mill Row men kept the game going on the Loughgall Road. The Row consisted of 50 odd, little houses with half doors built in the shadow of the big spinning mill of Drumcairne. Like the stone outside Dan Murphy's door in the old song, the Mill Row men would assemble each night at the corner and while a few played handball or cards, the rest arranged a singles or partner bullet score down to Scott's Corner for a couple of bob and as the game progressed past the Dead House (the morgue of the County Asylum) the cheers went up as someone made a good shot towards the White Gates corner. And so it went on.

The bullet of course, oftimes ploughed into the depths of the roadside ditch but then there was the great 'bullet finder' Harry McConnell, who had the uncanny knack of walking over and putting his hand on the lost bowl. In summer days Harry was forever eating dandelions and Wee Jack from the Mill Row opined that there must have been something in the dandelion juice that made Harry the top bullet-finder!

At the outbreak of the last war, Bill George the great road bowlsman went off and joined the North Irish Horse and served in North Africa. When the war was over he came home again and took up the bullet, never talking much of his soldiering exploits. Later he went to work in Wolverhampton and died there one Christmas Eve about twenty years ago. I was greatly saddened at the passing of my boyhood hero and friend. Today bullet throwing is as popular as ever but it is more organised with gradings and such. No longer does the law lift the bullet, and the local newspapers devote much space each week to the games. I don't think Bill George would have really liked it this way. In his heyday when a score was being set up, someone would go out to Cabragh or meet him on the road or in the town and ask if he'd throw so-and-so. And that was that.

County Cork produced top throwers such as Mick Barry, now retired. Theirs was a different style of throwing the bullet. Instead of taking a fairly long run-up to their mark, they took a few quick steps and delivered the bullet into the air spinning like a top and when it hit the road it was still gathering speed. At a sharp corner they'd lift it right over trees or hedge, landing it safe and sound to continue for a fine shot. Men like Mick Barry were hard to beat. Today the top throwers of Armagh like Mick Toal are still facing up to the champs from the roads around Bandon, both at home and away. And today they also travel to Dagenham in England to throw the bullet and also every year to Germany and Holland. A long way indeed from the tuppenny scores along the Lough-gall Road on a summer's night when I was a lad.

Tom's spy glasses

On the bright summer Saturday mornings of the thirties before the war broke out, when Tom the roadman came past our house on his way to the top of Stoops' Hill with his binoculars, I used to follow him down the loanen, across the bottom and up the steep hill, passing the solitary holly tree.

Tom's binoculars were the talk of the country. Tom swore they were so good you could have spotted a fly walking up the twin spires of St Patrick's Cathedral, a mile or so up the road in the city of Armagh. Tom never called them binoculars and like the rest of us referred to them as spy glasses. At that time in the mid-thirties, spy glasses were as rare to us country folk as a cinematograph for showing moving films. Tom thought a lot of his glasses and was reluctant even to let anyone take a look through them. He had saved for years out of his roadman's wages to buy them and he had travelled all the way to Belfast to get them in Smithfield.

When I followed Tom up to the top of the hill which had a commanding view away across the country to Lough Neagh and beyond to the mist-shrouded outline of the Sperrin Mountains which I used to think must have been in America, Tom knew I was coming behind him but he never looked back to call me on. He was a quiet man who kept himself to himself. When he reached the summit, he'd carefully take the spy glasses from their leather case, raise them to eye level, slowly adjust them to his own needs and stand there as still as a monument and there I'd be standing still, about twenty yards off, not daring to come any closer in case he'd let out a gulder at me and tell me to be off down the hill home. Then I would slowly edge towards him until eventually I was by his side and even then he didn't say 'So there ye are now.'

I would meekly say: 'Tom, do you see anything special away over there?' And maybe he wouldn't answer for five minutes or more. I remember the Saturday morning when we'd reached this stage and Tom lowered his glasses with a great expression of satisfaction on his weather-beaten face and exclaimed that he had the square of Dungannon town in focus and could make out the time on the town clock at the top of the square. Furthermore, if he wasn't seeing things, he added solemnly, there was a man standing on the right hand side of the clock tower and the man wore a cap.

From where we stood on that hill it must have been the best part of 20 miles to the town of Dungannon and that would be as the crow flies. Every Saturday morning Tom appeared to zoom right over to Dungannon, apparently ignoring the panoramic view which took in the villages of Moy, Blackwatertown and Benburb. There must have been something about Dungannon that acted as a magnet to his spy glasses.

All the way down the hill that morning he talked about seeing the clock in Dungannon, saying that the following Saturday if the weather remained suitable he would try his best to ascertain the time on the clock! Of course, I stared wide-eyed at him, adding that his glasses must indeed be the best spy glasses in all Ireland, to which he just gave a slight nod of the head. And so came the next Saturday, a bright, clear mid-summer morning. Tom at once got the glasses into focus on Dungannon and the clock and then he suddenly stiffened and shouted out loud: 'It's ten past ten on thon clock! I can see it as clear as the nose on your face! Ten past ten.' Then he quickly lowered the glasses and fished out his pocket watch and sure enough it was exactly ten past ten. 'Tom,' I cried, 'they are magic spy glasses you have. They must be when you can tell the time that far away.' Tom turned to me and gave me one of his rare smiles. 'They're powerful glasses and I have been trying for ages to make out the time on that clock away over in Dungannon. And I've done it this morning.'

He handed me the heavy glasses and said solemnly: 'Here, you can have a look through them and see if you can make out the time on thon clock.' I couldn't believe that he was really going to let me have a look through them; to look through that magic window at far-off fields.

With trepidation I grasped the spy glasses, raised them to eye-level and all at once I was suddenly transported into what seemed one of those time machines that H. G. Wells wrote about. I could have reached out and touched the railway line, half a mile off and could see Bob Johnson out feeding the hens beyond. Then slowly and carefully I raised the glasses in search of Dungannon. 'Up, up, up,' said Tom gently. 'You'll get no further than the Callan River if ye don't raise them.' Then the outline of a town made up a rather hazy picture, but I couldn't find the clock nor the clock tower, let alone anyone standing by wearing a cap. But even so, it was a real eye-opener for that muster of buildings away out there must indeed be the town of Dungannon. I stood there for what seemed ages taking in the picture, afraid to bat an eye in case the whole thing would disappear.

Tom took the glasses back. 'Well, how did it go?' 'I saw Dungannon, Tom, but I couldn't find the clock, but I believe I did see Lough Neagh and what appeared to be a little fishing boat.'

Tom looked at me incredulously. 'I don't believe you. You saw Lough Neagh and a fishing boat?'

'Aye, Tom, it was as clear as you like, but I couldn't find the clock in Dungannon.'

Tom mused. 'Ye know, I have also been trying for a long time to see a boat on Lough Neagh but so far I've been unable to do so.'

'It's true, Tom,' says I, 'I saw the fishing boat on Lough Neagh on the way back from Dungannon and the Sperrins.' I told Tom that if he looked directly over the top of the big tree behind Johnny Carroll's house and over the meadow he'd get a powerful view of the lough. Tom raised the glasses and stood there as if he were an astronomer on the track of a new star in the heavens. After ten minutes he gave up, put the glasses carefully back into the leather case and sat down on the grass. The lough, he said, was a bit of a haze to him, but he would try again next Saturday. 'From now on I'll give Dungannon a rest and look for a fishing boat on Lough Neagh. Will ye come up with me next Saturday morning?'

Well, the following Saturday came and went as did all of them during that lovely summer, but Tom failed to find a boat on Lough Neagh. 'Maybe it's my eyes. You're young and have strong eyes. Do ye think that's why?'

'Not at all, Tom,' I said, 'you have the best of eyes. Some of these days you'll find the boat on Lough Neagh.'

By the following summer Tom had moved house and did all his spying from the top of another hill a couple of miles away. Who knows, maybe what I saw that Saturday morning through Tom's magical glasses was a mirage. But to this day I firmly believe that Tom did see the clock in Dungannon at ten past ten that morning when the lark sang high over the meadow below.

Cutting pea-pods

Whenever I hear of point-to-point race meetings I think back to when I was a lad at school in the thirties and how I was deprived of going along to a day at the races, a point-to-point event held in the second week of April.

It wasn't that I was locked up in my room at home, mind you, but from the time I was nine years of age until I was 14, on every race day, you'd have found me out in the nearby little plantation or 'planton' as we called it, cutting pea-rods. Doing this chore was not out of choice and the person behind it was none other than the head-master of the school in the town that I attended. The galling thing about the annual pea-rod cutting affair was that the school had the half-day off to go to the races about a mile out of town and always held on a Wednes-day, for that was the day when all the shopboys and such had their half-day off work.

Just before the classes were dismissed before noon, the headmaster would, after cautioning the boys to be well behaved at the races, call me up to where he sat beside the open fireplace. 'Race day means pea-rod day again, eh, Rafferty boy?' I was one of the few country gulls in the town school and he always took it for granted that I would hardly wish to patronise the racing events away at the other end of the town. So he looked upon the half-day off as a golden opportunity for him to get some pea-rods for his large suburban garden.

It would be the same routine he told me. Cut four big bundles, secure them well; bring them home and then in a day or two when Anthony would call to deliver the weekly groceries at our house with his Shetland pony and small flat topped cart, he would collect the pea-rods and duly deliver them to him. Anthony was the delivery man for Barney the grocer in the town and the wee

Shetland and cart caught the eye of everyone. A lovely little, hard-working pony; well groomed; harness shining and fed like a member of Barney's own family.

Anyhow, when I got home shortly after noon and had a bite to eat, I took the billhook out and ventured forth to the 'planton' where for the next two hours or more I would cut selected branches of ash and hazel which I knew from experience would be suitable as pea-rods. Each one had to be strong and supple and be of a uniform length. I always brought Larry the black Labrador with me to the 'planton' and he'd hunt after waterhens and rabbits in the miniature jungle. Being an avid comic cuts reader, I imagined hacking my way through the tropical rain forests of South America, half-expecting Tarzan to come swinging through the higher trees, or being confronted by a ferocious wild animal. Thinking thus lightened the hard work of cutting the pea-rods. When I had my four large bundles ready, I had to trail them home up the road and up the loanen and leave them in the haggard where Anthony would duly collect them either the next day or the day after.

Back at the school the following day, the lads would be talking about the races and all I could talk about was cutting the pea-rods. 'Ah, ye didn't miss much,' said my pal Peter. 'Thon oul' horses couldn't run to keep themselves warm, so they couldn't. And sure the oul' jockeys were far too big and fat and heavy for the poor oul' nags.'

Usually on the following Saturday when I would be up the town on an errand, the headmaster would spot me and call me over. Then he'd put his hand into his trousers pocket and take out a fortune in silver and copper. 'They were good pea-rods, Rafferty boy. You did a good job and you will have to be rewarded.' And from the handful of silver and copper he would meticulously extract four pennies and hand them to me as if he were giving me the world. 'There now. That's for your work well done. Don't spend it too foolishly.' . . .

That fourpence would buy two bags of chocolate drops, or maybe one bag and a comic cut called *The Adventure*.

Salute to an old custom

I am led to believe that the younger generation these times never give what we used to call a 'salute' to a clergyman along the street or country road. Today the poor man of the cloth, of whatever denomination, hardly merits a glance, let alone a salute, whereas in the thirties and forties you'd have raised your cap or given a short salute to his Reverence.

I, like many others of my time, was brought up to respect a clergyman, minister or priest, even if he was in a car and me on the old bicycle. One day a clergyman from the local rectory came into our house for a bit of a chat as he oftimes did when passing along the road. A fine gentleman he was too, kindly and with a good word for every one of God's children. He told my mother that 'the Rafferty boys' always gave him a salute along the road, but only a few of his own church members did likewise.

My mother had always told us to show respect to a clergyman. At the same time, however, I remember some clergymen and when you'd give them a salute, they'd just give you a look. Perhaps they had their mind on higher things at the time, so I should not be harsh in my judgement. During the years of my youth, saluting a clergyman was more of a custom in the country than in the town, although there were rural fellows who'd have hidden behind the hedge until his Reverence passed by in case he asked some questions that would be a trifle hard to answer, honestly, that is. At that time if a chap was keeping company with a girl, the clergy always got to know about it and were not backwards in coming forward to ask Johnny if his intentions were honourable or something like that, questions that were inclined to be difficult to answer at times. One priest in the town when

16

I was taking lessons on the violin, was a great man for music and his choir in the cathedral was reckoned second to none. One evening on my way home with fiddle case tucked under my arm, didn't I meet him. He there and then stopped me and began to demonstrate with the aid of his big black umbrella the correct way to bow the fiddle. People in the street stood and stared and to tell the truth I did not feel all that comfortable being in such a spotlight, for there were a few of my school pals in the audience and I swear I could hear them giggle. But there was his Reverence bowing majestically with his umbrella. I'll never forget that lesson.

He was a tall, solemn cleric who was never known to smile, let alone laugh, most of the boys gave the Canon a wide berth because as they said there was no codding with him. However, he never failed to acknowledge your salute and always lifted his black hat in response. One summer evening he was out for a walk along the road and although the sun was splitting the trees he had his big black brolly slung over his arm. It came to pass that he came upon a poor roadman cutting the hedge and grass with billhook and hook. Pausing for a chat it turned out that the roadman played a bit on the violin himself so naturally the Canon was immediately interested. After plying your man with musical questions he invited him to call at the parochial house on the following Saturday afternoon, the roadman's half-day. He told him to bring his violin with him as he was anxious to hear him render a short recital. So your man, come Saturday, dickied himself up with his Sunday suit and headed for the parochial house with the fiddle strapped on the carrier of the bicycle.

On arrival, the housekeeper ushered Mick into the room and soon the solemn Canon entered and walked right over to the window and kept looking out. 'Now,' says he, in his deep, resounding voice, 'let us hear what you can play on your violin.' The roadman, now wishing he hadn't come at all, tuned up the fiddle, rosined the bow and began playing a selection of his favourite pieces, a jig, a reel, a hornpipe, 'Danny Boy,' 'Mountains of Mourne' and a Scottish schottische called 'Tam Says the Divil's Dead.'

When finished he stood there waiting for the verdict. 'Well, Canon, what d'ye think o' my playing?' he asked timidly. The Canon turned slowly and gave him a hard piercing look. 'My good fellow, you play like the Derryfubble Flute Band. You have neither time, tone or rhythm.' That was it. The Canon then marched out of the room leaving the poor roadman to let himself out.

A week afterwards, the roadman told a friend of his musical experience with the Canon. Says he: 'Ye know something? I used to think I was a right oul' fiddler, but now I know I have a lot to learn and I'm practising a lot in my spare time.'

Anyhow, whether you fiddle a bit or not, I still think we should show respect to men of the cloth. Giving the 'salute' is something I would like to make a comeback, especially among the young ones, but when you look around you today in this age of tinned beer and pop, it's hard to visualise. However, today the clergy and the young are on much more familiar terms than we'd have dreamt of in our youth. They can talk to priest or minister 'man to man' as Spencer Tracy playing Father Flanagan told Pee Wee in the film 'Boys' Town.' And that's a good thing. We country lads were afraid to open our mouth to them half the time. Fifty years or so ago lads were always expected to 'salute' the teacher outside as a mark of respect. On reflection, I believe some of them didn't deserve it, but no matter.

But some incidents have a lasting effect. Anytime I take a scrape on the old Stradivarius these times, I can see the tall black figure of the Canon standing in the street bowing with his black umbrella – and you know, I always endeavour to use the bow likewise, and I raise my cap to him for that, at any rate.

Talking about playing the fiddle. Tommy was a well known player in our part of the country and used to call to make his ceili. We'd all sit waiting to hear a couple of good tunes, as my brother John was also a fiddle player and a mate of Tommy. But Tommy would take his fiddle out of the case and start tuning it. Then he'd stop and start yarning about something or other and start rosining the bow. And all this tuning and rosining the bow would go on for maybe twenty minutes or more before Tommy actually got down to playing. He was a 'lug' player, that is he didn't read a note of music but played all by ear, which is a gift you are born with, I was told. When Tommy did get started he was hard to stop and would have played till the cows come home.

Lost chords of a bygone age to be sure.

The man with the dog

It is said that a man's best friend is his dog and truth is there are many men along the highways and byways of Ulster, in towns and villages who would venture forth without their boots rather than without the dog, be it a Jack Russell or an Abysinnian Growler. Many things have changed in this day and age but no matter where you wander you will always come across the man with his dog. And in many parts of the country a certain man will be referred to as 'the man with the dog,' for no matter what the season he will be out and about with his pal.

I have always thought that as time goes by, either the man gets more like the dog or the dog gets more like the man. And again the man walks like his dog and the dog walks like his master. I've often watched an old black Labrador, blunt of tooth, barely able to put one foot past the other just like his old mate, well in the winter of life. And look you closely at the dog and you will notice that the eagerness in his eye has long since vanished and his curiosity for life and what is round the next corner doesn't mean a thing, just like his old friend who has seen all there is to see and maybe more. If perchance a rabbit should dash out across his path the dog may give a short asthmatic bark and dander on, barely raising an eye at all. They're two of a kind, walking into the sunset.

In summer when the man sits down by the wayside the dog will sit down also. You can never be sure whether the man is taking the dog for a walk or the dog is taking the man for a walk. But just you stop and take a good look at them. Doesn't one act exactly like the other? I knew an old woman up the country in my young days and she was the spitting image of her old parrot kept in a gilded cage in the cottage by the roadside where the cuckoo called in the spring and the curlew in the winter. And I've seen men who look like their sheepdogs, King Charles Spaniels, rough-haired terriers and the Lassie-Come-Home breed. And the man walking the grey-hound is as skinny and sharp featured as his dog on the lead.

I take my cap off to the man with the dog. In no way are they a dying breed.

Happily I grew up in the good company of dogs. The first one I can recall was Larry the Labrador who slept at night behind a haystack in the haggard. He had been a good hunting dog in his prime when my father took him out for a shot with the gun over Drummanmore hills outside Armagh.

In his old age he developed a constant cough and I used to lie out with him behind the haystack to keep him company.

There was Sweeper the black Labrador who came as a young dog later and had endless energy, always looking for me to take him away down the meadow for a gallop. He loved the river and splashed and swam through it like a fish, chasing waterhens and rabbits in wild abandon. At the same time we had Bo the little rough-haired terrier, a prim and proper little fellow who loved to hunt with Sweeper, scouring the hedges for the elusive rabbit.

One summer morning Bo got knocked down by a passing goods train on the nearby railway and lay at death's door for a couple of weeks. In the house I made a bed for him complete with a pillow and he lay there on his side almost motionless. Then one day he staggered to his feet and propping himself against the wall of the house, made it outside and for the next four days or so he kept walking round an outhouse, leaning against it until finally he could walk unaided. Bo had one bad habit; he sucked eggs and of course when I caught him in the act I endeavoured not to let my parents known about it, for in the country at that time it was a cardinal sin for a dog to

suck an egg. One morning I went out to call Bo but he
appeared to have flown the coop and the family seemed
as mystified about his disappearance as I was. The
following day my father told me in solemn tones that
Davy the railway track walker had spotted Bo racing
away over the hills for some unknown reason. Well I
searched the countryside but there was no sign of Bo. He
had done a bunk as my elder brother surmised sagely. A
year later I learned the truth. My father had observed Bo
sucking eggs for a couple of days, so when the turfman
called he gave him Bo. My father told me that Bo just had
to go, as an egg-sucking dog could not be kept round the
house, but he assured me that the turfman would give
him a good home. I later wondered if the turfman kept
laying hens?

Mind you I cried when alone for a long time after Bo
had gone. It's hard to part with a good friend. And the
grief was just becoming bearable when poor Sweeper
died. I went out one morning before going to school and
found him dead in his house. For a long time Sweeper's
house was a big wooden barrel, cowped on its side and
filled with hay and straw. There were winter evenings
when I crawled into the barrel and lay with Sweeper and
my mother would come out and say anxiously: 'Come in
this minute or you'll get your death of cold.' Of course I
never felt the cold in Sweeper's house at all, even when
winter winds were howling outside.

I had many other dogs, all good and sure friends and
on Saturdays we'd head off early through the hills, not
returning until dusk, feeding on nuts, apples and berries
in the time of year. I never went anywhere without a dog
and I'm sure the people in the district called me 'the boy
with the dog.'

At night we brought our dog into the house to lie at the
fireside and they all lapped this up except Sweeper, who
couldn't content himself long enough but had to be out
tearing round the house barking at the least sound, or

chasing the neighbour's cat down the loanen. Many a time now as I sit over a winter fire I imagine I can hear Sweeper bark in the distance. But it's well over fifty years since Sweeper barked for the last time.

The ice-cream man on the bike

I remember the sunny summers of boyhood and the ice-cream man who travelled the roads on his bicycle, selling sliders and pokes, penny ones and tuppenny ones.

You might be dandering along the road or turning hay in a field and your tongue hanging out with the heat and then the miracle would happen and it was no mirage either. Down the road would come the ice-cream man all in white, pedalling along at his leisure on the bike and if you had a couple of pence in your pocket you were landed.

He had a big drum of lovely ice-cream on the special bicycle and you always got good value for money. For the slider, he used a little trowel, wielding it with the skill of a plasterer and pokes were sprinkled with a dash of red flavouring stuff, delicious to the parched palate. The ice-cream man never hurried himself and making the slider or poke was a ritual with which he took great pains.

At times, coming out of Armagh he wouldn't get past the Mill Row corner on the Loughgall Road before he was sold out. There was always a pitch and toss school or a gathering engaged in debating matters of the world. Then on down the road, the lads throwing a game of bullets would descend on him like a swarm of bees.

People working at the haymaking put a handful of oaten meal into a bucket of water and this kept it fresh and cool. Buttermilk, of course was and still is, the great thirst quencher but no one in their senses in the country would dream of taking a drink of buttermilk on a very hot summer day. They said it could well kill you before the night was out if you did partake of it, or at least give you cramps that would have you crawling up the walls all night. Buttermilk on a hot day was the quare boy, as they said.

I recall one quiet little man of the roads who'd call at our house in the heat of summer and timidly ask for a drink of buttermilk. That was all he ever wanted and you never saw him when the summer ended.

But back to the ice-cream man on the bike. He was certainly a welcome sight on the roads of summer long ago, a figure, alas, now gone like our youth too soon.

And the ice-cream parlours in the town were an oasis on a hot summer day or night when you'd be going to the pictures. There you could buy a poke as big as a haystack for a tanner. Come the dark, cold, frosty nights of winter, my friend Pat and I called at the parlours, not for ice-cream, but for a big mug of Bovril which, as one local man put it: 'would do your heart and soul good.'

The goods clerks who never sat down

Many a morning and evening I stood and watched them standing at their desks with pen in hand; stern looking clerks in the goods office at the railway station. At that time in the thirties I left my bicycle inside the goods store at the station each morning about half-eight and then walked the short distance up the town to school. I was the only lad allowed this privilege of leaving the bike there and I got the special dispensation because I came from a railway family.

The goods store was a hive of activity with the long, flat horse-drawn Wordie carts and breadcarts filling up for the day. The Belfast firm of Wordie were carriers, well known the length and breadth of the north. I can still smell that rich aroma of meal, bread and porter, for then all the drink came by train and the large barrels of porter were delivered by the Wordie men.

The goods office was at the end of the store and you could see the four clerks at their work, always standing up at their desks, keeping account of all merchandise that passed through the store. The clerks were over-lorded by a bearded man who looked like George Bernard Shaw. The chief clerk walked briskly to and from work, most times walking right in the middle of the street, oblivious to cars blowing their horns or cyclists ringing their bells. He had been in the army and was a stickler for neatness and punctuality. And they said that this chief clerk had a fountain of knowledge and with it a grand fountain pen, the equal of which wasn't to be had in the whole country. At that time ink wells were used in such offices and in schools. The other clerks used the ordinary slim nibbed pen that you could have bought for a few pennies.

When I'd be coming home from school the goods store

clerks would still be standing there, writing away furiously. An important job, surely: every item had to be invoiced and entered in the appropriate ledger, details of which were then passed on to the head office of the Great Northern Railway.

The goods wagons were shunted right up through the centre of the store where they were duly loaded or unloaded. The big wooden barrels of porter were rolled expertly by the storemen, a genuine display of rolling out the barrel and it was rumoured that many a pint was syphoned off to relieve the burden of a hot summer day. And a storeman once told me that a barrel began to leak unnoticed and the upshot of it was that a couple of store rats, as big as cats who led the good life there, ended up drunk with the porter, staggering all over the place, like Oul' Jemmy going home on the half-ten bus on a Saturday night.

I often watched the breadmen fill up their carts in the morning from all the different bakeries in Belfast – McCombs, McWatters, Barney Hughes, Inglis, etc. They were all in a hurry to be out and away and many a morning too, I was given a couple of lovely fresh buns, a Paris bun or better still, a currant square, which I put in my schoolbag and ate at lunchtime.

This was in the heyday of the G.N.R. when a station was the life blood of a town. Alas, that has long since gone and many a goods store lies derelict from Armagh to Belfast. I do not know what way freight is handled by rail these times, but I'm sure the clerks don't stand up at their desks all day – and if there are still chief clerks, I don't think they would wield a fountain pen anymore. And the rollicking Wordie carts have long since disappeared from the streets of Ulster's towns. Many of today's stations do not look like railway stations at all: Lisburn must be one of the few still looking the part. But even here, there is no such thing as a waiting room anymore, and the signal cabins are replaced by computerised rooms from which the signalman cannot see outside. Not the rail McCoy, I'd say . . .

The daylight ghost train

As a lad living among the orchardlands of County Armagh, I never had any reason to be afraid of the Ghost Train. The Great Northern Railway ran past our house, a level crossing house at Reilly's Rocks, a mile out of Armagh station on the line to Portadown and on to Belfast.

The Ghost Train was the little diesel, buggy-like machine that transported the gang of platelayers and their tools along the track.

This stretch of line was lifted in 1957 and the people gathered in great numbers one November night to see the very last train go by. The days of the big hissing locos were over: engines named after Irish mountains and rivers and birds of prey – such as Sugar Loaf, Lugnaquilla, Slieve Donard, Falcon, Slieve Gullion. Now the track is a wilderness and local farmers have moved in and wired sections off for grazing. The surrounding area is now a great sanctuary for wild life, where the hare and the rabbit run free and wild strawberries grow in profusion in June.

I grew up with the trains, one of the 'Railway Children' of the thirties and the puffers were my timepiece when I'd be out through the fields with my dogs, Larry the Labrador and Bo the rough-haired terrier. During the 1939–45 war there was an engine driver who was the born spit of Adolf Hitler, down to his moustache and hairstyle. And when he was off for a break in Armagh and dandered through the town, people stood and stared at him, wondering how on earth oul' Shicklegruber himself had managed to get to the primatial city of Armagh! But Matt McShane, as he was called was no Hitler, but the gentlest man in the world. He knew that he resembled Adolf and enjoyed playing the role where he wasn't known.

The platelaying gang responsible for the line between Armagh and Richhill, were not only skilled workers, but were also musicians and storytellers, the last of a dying race. There were fiddlers, a banjo player, a harmonica or French fiddler and a drummer who could also make music on a hair comb by means of placing paper over it and blowing through the teeth. Easier said than done. When they'd be working near our house they had their midday tea boiled on our big black Modern Mistress stove and if the weather was inclement they'd troop in and have their repast round the fire. 'Railwaymen's Tay' made in a large tin with a wire handle was widely known as the strongest brew imaginable, stronger in fact, than 'Roadmen's Tay.' And not only was it brewed but boiled until it bubbled like an active volcano. In summer days it was brewed up over a fire of twigs along the railway banks.

Davy, the ganger, came from Sleepy Valley in the old world village of Richhill and his lunch consisted of well-baked griddle soda farls with an ample covering of butter. Davy always occupied the best chair in the house at the fireside during winter days when biting winds blew down from Drummanmore Hill. He had been a trackwalker for some years between Armagh station and Richhill, a distance of six miles. His job was to make sure the lines were safe and sound and this being the era when wooden 'keys' were used on the 'chair' linking one rail with another, Dave carried a bagful of spare keys slung over his shoulder alongside his heavy hammer. Walking that distance twice a day whetted the appetite so Davy was always in need of a taste of tea as he passed our house, for he was a good friend of the family. He used to say that a man could really be at peace with the world walking along the railway track early of a summer morning when the birds sang all around. A man, he said, had time to think and he firmly believed in what the poet Thomas Hood wrote: 'What is this life if full of care, we have not time to stand and stare . . .'

John was the next trackwalker when Davy was promoted to ganger. He too, was oftimes hailed into the house for a drop of tea. He hadn't the romantic soul of Davy and was forever complaining of the loneliness of the long-distance railway trackwalker where your only companion in winter was the cold call of the curlew. John had one irritating habit – he was forever rattling his loose false teeth, but he was a great bearer of all the latest news from around the town and countryside. Anything he hadn't heard about wasn't worth hearing about. You had little need of the weekly newspaper when John was trackwalking.

Jemmy who drove the Ghost Train was a respected traditional fiddler and also made the famous Lambeg drums at his home at Ballyards, a few miles south of Armagh City. And although Jemmy was proud to wear his sash and walk on the 'Twelfth Day' he was equally at home at a ceilidhe with his beloved jigs, reels and hornpipes.

His method of making the Lambeg drum was his well guarded secret, but he did divulge that well seasoned goatskin was needed. He had also made about half-a-dozen violins himself and had sold them and I'm sure they are still being played and if not, hanging on a wall somewhere. During the lunch break in our house he would take down my brother John's fiddle and play a medley of Irish tunes in his rich traditional style of staccato bowing. He'd sit with the fiddle perched over one knee and his heavy boots keeping time on the oilcloth-covered floor. He could have talked about music all day, what with his quavers, semiquavers, demisemiquavers and yes, even hemidemisemiquavers!

Sam the tall, quiet man with bushy moustache and cap, never smiled all that much and he rode his bicycle daily to and from Markethill, a good ten miles each direction and like the others in the gang was on the job at 7.30 each morning, whatever the weather. Sam was also a violin player, but with a less flamboyant style than the bold Jemmy. Although an 'ear' player, Sam held the instrument in the correct position under his chin and his bowing had a fine flow to it. It was about that time that I took up learning to play the violin, an instrument I have loved all my life, so I was sitting up and taking notice of players and their individual styles.

Frank the banjoist had also a fine tenor voice and in his younger days had graced the stage at concerts in Armagh. He was the last of the trackwalkers and on fine summer mornings and misty autumn days he'd come whistling along the lines with his hammer slung over his shoulder.

A couple of miles below our place was the Retreat Halt, the only railway station in all Ireland where the 'stationmaster' carried the platform around on his back! It was not listed as a station in the company's books and John Cunningham was the man in charge. He stayed in a little black wooden hut and opened and closed the crossing gates manually across the tracks. And anyone boarding a train or alighting did so via a set of wooden steps which John placed in the appropriate position. A veteran of the First World War, he could converse in French and Flemish and during World War Two when Belgian troops were stationed in Armagh City, John was often called upon to act as interpreter, something of which he was very proud indeed. He rode his bicycle to work from his home in Armagh to the Retreat Halt, a distance of five miles and being an old soldier kept his uniform spick and span and, as they said, you could have seen yourself in the shine of his shoes.

Occasionally I go back to walk where the railway lines used to be and as I dander along the quiet ways I see in the mind's eye, the stalwart platelaying gang, the sound of Jemmy's fiddle playing resonantly 'The Pigeon on the Gate' or 'The Maid Behind the Bar.' And whist! Is that the Ghost Train coming down by Mullinure Bridge? No, the musical railway gang are all dead and gone long since. If there are such things as ghosts (there is a belief that most railwaymen return to earth as crows), then I feel sure that the spirits of Davy, Jemmy, John, Sam and Jim the signalman are still around, even if they did go and lift the lines over 30 years ago.

LONG BEFORE THE TEABAG CAME

Dropping into Sam's shop

Time was when a chap could have carried a parcel under his oxter and held his head high. That was when shops used good, strong brown wrapping paper fastened with cord that you could have laced your boots with. If you were in town to purchase a pair of shoes, boots, simmit or shirt or a pair of trousers, they'd have wrapped them up in a man's parcel that could be put on the carrier or handlebars of the bike. These times it's all these fancy plastic bags and no matter what shop you go to they put everything into one and send you out to shame the face off you. Years ago, a man wouldn't have carried such a thing for fear of being called an oul' woman or worse.

In the thirties and forties in Armagh there were some men who wouldn't have been caught dead carrying even a well wrapped brown parcel. They'd try to conceal it as best they could and if they weren't in a big hurry home they'd park it in the likes of Sam Wright's shop or Quigley's sweetie shop. Sam Wright was a wee man who gave customers the impression that he detested standing behind the counter. He had a row of shelves round the spacious store and sold everything from the proverbial needle to five Woodbines and a quarter ounce of snuff.

If you asked him for some article that chanced to be on the higher shelves, Sam would either tell you to call back on your way home or else take the big step ladder and tell you to go get it yourself, while he stood there smoking Park Drive and gazing out through the window.

He was inclined to look with distrust at his big step ladder. Once he had climbed to the top rung to get some washing soda, the ladder went into a wobble and Sam fell off. He spilled the washing soda all over the place and was laid up for a spell. I was often sent to get black lead for giving our Dover and later the Modern Mistress stove a bit of a shine. If luck was with me as a ten-year-old-boy, Sam would have it near his hand but again at times the black lead was on a high shelf and I had to make the precarious ascent on the oul' shaking ladder to get it myself.

Sam did a roaring trade with the snuff and the old dolls draped in shawls from the Banbrook Hill area were never out of the shop and I used to gaze in wonderment at Sam weighing out the pungent snuff on the small set of scales. He was a dab hand at it. He usually put the snuff in paper pokes which he expertly made himself. Just try making a paper cone yourself and you'll probably be all fingers.

Sam lived out the road apiece and travelled on a trusty bicycle. He never had much of a window display, maybe a few empty Persil boxes or a big advertisement for 'Players Please' or another for pipe tobacco which read: 'The sensible man smokes Crowbar.' Chances were if you asked him for a plug of Crowbar he'd tell you he didn't stock it. He could be rather contrary in ways. When I chanced to be in the shop near closing time Sam would send me up to the Shambles Corner to take a good look at the sky out that direction and then come back and tell him if it looked like rain for maybe that was the day he had forgotten to bring his top coat. You felt a right Charlie standing up the street looking up in the air to see if there were any dark clouds around and some of the lads hanging round the corner at Barney O'Neill's shop watching you, thinking you were away in the head or something.

Sam's shop was certainly the Old Curiosity Shop of the City of Armagh and he himself was very much in the mould of a Dickensian character. He made a point of telling people about Customer Conn. This was a tall, quiet man who came into town two or three days a week from out the Moy Road. He'd wheel his bicycle into Sam's shop and right down into the store at the rear and then without a how-do-ye-do to Sam walked out and away up the street. I chanced to be there one day when this happened.

'Ye see him? That's Customer Conn. He comes in here, wheels the oul' bike through the shop and parks it back there in the store. And if he had to buy a box of matches he'd get them in McKinney's up the street there. He has never given me tuppence for the past couple of years. Some of these days I'm gonna tell him to park the oul' bicycle somewhere else. Sometimes he comes back with a good few parcels, but never spends a make here.'

That was Customer Conn. He must have thought Sam's shop was a right-of-way and the store a public parking place. As Sam said some people had the quare neck on them.

To the average country chap in the thirties and forties carrying parcels was almost as bad as carrying an umbrella. If it was raining you took your ducking like a man for at that time the only men who carried umbrellas were the swanks, dandies, bank clerks and clergymen.

I recall standing with a few of the lads up the town one day when this fellow strode by swinging his brolly like Beau Brummell and it a lovely May evening with the swallows circling overhead. 'Would ye luk at that oul' cod acting' the swank and him without tuppence to jingle in his pockets,' quipped Drumcairne Pat, sucking at the butt of a Woodbine. We knew the brolly man, a decent enough chap he was, but a bit carried away, maybe on account of seeing too many pictures in the Cosy Corner Picture House. The sages round and about would solemnly tell you that the pictures had driven many a man to the bad, because Armagh and the Moy and Blackwatertown and Richhill was a different world altogether from the make-believe world of Hollywood U.S.A. and a man had to keep his feet planted steady on *terra firma*.

Worse still was the fellow in the town who wore kid

gloves and carried an umbrella when the sun was splitting the trees in Dobbin's Flowery Vale. And they were
real summers then mind you before all this talk about the
ozone layer and such which if you listened to it all would
put you round the bend. Why any mortal man wore kid
gloves on a hot summer day was completely beyond our
understanding. Very few of us lads ever owned a pair of
kid gloves and you were lucky if you had a pair of
ninepenny woollen ones out of Woolworths which were
the great man for the bike in the winter.

A chap who lived down our way had a big umbrella
but never appeared with it in daylight. He was a great
man for heading up the road for the last house of the
pictures and on a winter night he'd take the brolly but
hid it in the hedge before he got to the Mill Row and the
lights, for fear of anyone seeing him. Even if it was
raining heavily the brolly would go into the hole in the
hedge and on he'd proceed with the rain battering into
him. On the way home he would collect the umbrella.

Mullinure Tom never liked stepping out for the first
time in a new suit of clothes for he thought everyone
would be staring at him and talking about him, God help
his wit when I look back on it. So before making his debut
in a new suit (which wasn't all that often) Tom hung the
suit out on the clothesline behind the house and
hammered it with a big stick until there wasn't a sign of a
crease left and it wasn't like a brand new rig at all.

I have known a few characters from country areas and
they were heart afraid of being seen coming out of
Cafolla's fish and chip shop. They thought that if anyone
spotted them they'd think so-and-so mustn't get a bite at
home when he has to go for something to eat in the town.
We are an odd race in many ways in this part of the
world, the island of saints and scholars. Every time we
go down on our knees we are not necessarily praying.
More often than not and this applies mainly in rural
areas, we are endeavouring to 'duke' someone who is

passing on the other side of the ditch. Not that we may have any reason for doing so but this behaviour is inherent in some of us and it is hard to break old customs.

Ned lived beside a railway bridge and he let the hedges grow as high as possible so that he would be almost invisible to the naked eye. Every time he spotted anyone approach he dived into the house and bolted the door in case they'd be thinking of calling on him. When he had occasion to venture out on an errand into the town he waited until a train was coming full belt under the bridge, throwing up a cloud of smoke. Then he'd make a run for it – over the bridge in the smoke and down the narrow road – with the result that his nearest neighbour never witnessed his coming or going. On the return journey he might have had to wait for half an hour or more until train time when he could get back into the house in a cloud of smoke. If Ned was still living in the same place at present he'd be in a bit of a predicament for they have long since lifted the railway lines and the bridge has been levelled to the ground.

But back to the brown paper parcels. I used to stand and marvel at the shopboys (some of them were ready for the pension) as they displayed the art of wrapping up a parcel, say a pair of boots or shoes, or shirt, or trousers or suit. With amazing dexterity in no time at all they would have a neat parcel, expertly tied with strong white cord, as tight as a fiddle string, flawlessly manipulated to the very last knot. It was a treat to watch the shopboys of fifty years ago. And mind you, the shopboys were highly respected members of the community who always dressed to perfection. Why, some of them even wore kid gloves and carried an umbrella when there was no sign of rain.

Filling in the ration books

You have only to look at the faces of people doing their shopping these times to know that it is all a bit of a chore, even if there's not a bite in the cupboard. Supermarkets may be handy enough but the personal touch isn't there at all. Time was when you were a customer of a grocer's shop you were treated as something of a V.I.P., but now you are just one of the throng. However, the supermarket is very hygienic and years ago when the grocer would be cutting you a few slices of bacon, he might just be after stroking the oul' dog at the door, not that I'm hinting that a looked-after dog is not clean, mind you.

I remember when my family 'daled' with a grocer by the name of Barney Fox in Armagh. His was a small shop; just himself and the good missus and they had a wee Shetland pony and wee flat van to deliver the goods, sometimes far out into the country. Barney was a meticulous man and took great pains in carrying out his duties behind the counter, always attired in a spotless white apron, crisply starched. He treated his customers with the utmost respect and if their order included some item he hadn't in stock, then he'd promptly send his part-time errand boy to dash up the town on his bicycle to procure it elsewhere.

Barney's errand boy was, in fact, a big grown man, who drove the Shetland pony and van. The errand boy was named Anthony and when despatched away out the road with a few orders, Anthony was never averse to killing time on the job. In summer you could see the wee pony graze by the wayside while Anthony stretched himself out on a mossy bank to enjoy a cigarette.

I took our weekly order into Barney's shop and the list never varied that much in the thirties – tea, sugar, bacon, butter, lard, flour with the weekly treat of a delicious slab cake. Barney didn't stock a variety of sweets, just bars of dark brown chocolate at a penny, tuppence and three-pence a bar.

He had his 'office' at the corner of the counter and on the sloping desk kept his set of books, including the large ledger, entering each transaction in beautiful copper-plate handwriting with a pen into which was inserted the nib of his choice. Barney was well versed in the prin-ciples of book-keeping, the rules of the ledger being 'IN DEBIT' 'OUT CREDIT.' He was so precise, ruling off here and there with a long wooden ruler.

During the early years of the war when there were coupons for the 'rations,' Barney often asked me to sit down on an onion box and fill in the details on all his customers' ration books. I wasn't allowed behind the counter into the 'office.' A tedious job, but I rather enjoyed it, knowing all the people who had their ration books with Barney. My reward for filling in all the names and addresses was a bar of chocolate – a threepenny bar. Then I'd go off home down the road, walking or on the bike, munching my chocolate with relish. It made me feel rather important to be asked to fill in the ration books.

Barney's life was built around his shop. And come night, summer and winter, he'd dress in his good suit complete with hard hat (bowler that is) and ride his bike through the town to inspect the window displays. He was also responsible for the task of seeing that all other shops closed trading at the proper time, so he was a sort of shop inspector. He'd stand there, staring at a window display, taking stock, perhaps getting a hint on how to dress his own window.

At an early age I used to stand in the shop and watch Barney packing his shelves, handling each article as if it was pure gold. I often wondered if Barney the grocer had harboured other ambitions – perhaps being manager of one of the big shops in the town like the Diamond Dairy, Liptons or Quinns. But now looking back I realise that

Barney Fox, grocer and provisions merchant, must have been a man contented with his lot in life. He opened at nine in the morning and closed on the dot of six, also closing half-day every Wednesday when he again took his inspection tour of the town to make sure that other shops were also observing the half-day closing.

Today when I'm in a supermarket I find myself wishing I were back in Barney's shop when life was at a more leisurely pace.

Long before the teabag came

Bill the shopboy rode up and down the road each day to his work in the town, with a half-day on Wednesday. At that time they were all known as shopboys no matter what age they were. Bill was a tall athletic fellow who spent his Sundays walking half the country with his friend and neighbour, a civil servant, also called Bill. They always stepped out in fine style, each with a big flower in their lapel in the summertime.

Bill the shopboy was a professional at the job in a shop called The Diamond Dairy in the days when a lad, leaving school, had to serve long years of apprenticeship to the grocery and provision trade, starting off with wages of five shillings a week. Many a time as a schoolboy I was despatched up the town to get odds and ends of groceries in the big shop where Bill worked. I always admired how he went about the job behind the counter and it was a treat to watch him manipulate the bacon slicer or cutting a pound of cheese with a strong string and especially weighing out tea and sugar. Tea and sugar were kept in large barrel-like affairs and Bill, with a silver trowel, could fill a half pound or pound bag on the scales in no time, right down to the last correct ounce. And the same with sugar.

There was a lovely aroma of the 'loose' tea as it was packed. Then with the correct amount in the brown bag, with deft fingers he closed the top firmly and at that time there was no sellotape, mind you. He always wore a white shirt, tie, and white apron and he moved about behind the counter with the agility and ease of a trained shopboy.

Flour for baking was also made up in a similar manner and my mother, who did a lot of homebaking on the griddle, usually bought her flour in stones and a stone bag of flour was a tricky thing to convey safely home on the carrier of the bicycle. Coffee was not as popular with the ordinary country folk then and only the swanks in the town drank coffee, but now and then we used to get a bottle of the liquid Camp coffee which I found rather too sweet and the family was never all that partial to it, so a bottle would last us for ages.

The Diamond Dairy opened like all other big shops at nine in the morning and closed on the dot of six. Bill went home for his dinner from one to two, on his three-speed shiny bike, a distance of two miles down the road. Along our stretch of the road there were very few white collar workers and the men working in the fields used to say: 'There's Bill away up the road, he has the quare job. Never has to dirty his hands.'

Barney the barman cycled from Ballynick. He was always rigged out in a neat blue pinstripe and a soft hat, hard collar and he looked more like the men you'd see in the pictures. Barney was one of the town's best known barmen, and although sombre looking he had a great sense of humour. His great fear in life was wicked dogs, since the day a big black dog jumped out of the ditch and tore the leg off his trousers. I recall the day along the road when Barney displayed for me the art of inflating a bicycle tube and tyre correctly. There I was pumping away and getting nowhere, when Barney stops, takes the pump in his hands and in no time the tyre was as hard as a rock. But back to the dogs. They were the plague of his life and it appeared that every dog in the townland had it in for Barney.

It is believed by some, of course, that a dog knows fine well if you are afraid of it and will play up on you as a result. Barney swore that all dogs, big and small, were vicious.

When the horse ran away with the bread

The day Eddie the breadman's horse did a quick bunk with the breadcart when a blizzard blew up is still well remembered by the remaining older hands around Salter's Grange and Reilly's Rocks on the Loughgall Road outside Armagh. The whole episode illustrates rather dramatically that you can never be sure of what's going on in a horse's head. Furthermore, Eddie the breadman was a good horseman and could stand on the high side-step of the breadcart and whistle and sing to the band playing, with old faithful Charlie doing something between a Military Two-Step and the Piper's Jig along the highway.

Some folk said that Eddie could even talk horsey language but whether this was the case or not he was well liked by all his customers in town and country. He was a good breadman but in those days in the thirties there was no quibbling over the price of a loaf. It was usually left to Eddie as to what each customer's needs were, so when you went out to the cart he just handed you maybe two, three or a 'ticket' of plain loaves and half a dozen Paris buns or whatever, and that was that. He called round our way Tuesdays and Fridays and always appeared to be in a hurry and didn't dally long at each call; not like Andy the breadman who called on Wednesdays and Saturdays and would have sat down on the mossy bank, lit up a fag and yarned away. Andy was never in a hurry.

Anyhow, about the day in question when Charlie the horse did a bunk. It blew up a bit of a blizzard and as we used to say when we were young they must have been 'plucking geese in Heaven' for the snow came tumbling down thick and fast. Eddie the breadman had braved all weathers on the job, sitting up atop the cart or standing

lower down on the side-step. When the blizzard was
going well on this afternoon as he was travelling along a
narrow road, he decided to get down and walk behind
the cart for a spell and get a little shelter. He had done
this many a time before in snow, sleet and rain. So down
he climbs and began walking behind, while Charlie
cantered on apparently unaware. And on they both went
into the biting teeth of snow and wind with Eddie
thankful for the modicum of shelter behind the breadcart. His hands were almost frozen and he began clapping them together in an effort to get the old circulation
going again. But Charlie must have been scared by the
clapping of hands in the snow and he took to his heels
and away like a blaze of whins with the breadcart swaying behind him, leaving Eddie standing there in the
snow, totally dumbfounded, not taking it in that trusted
Charlie would do such a thing on him.

Eddie shouted and whistled, but all in vain. Soon
Charlie and the breadcart had disappeared round the
sharp bend, away down the Wee Well Hill and out onto
the road at Reilly's Rocks Corner. Muttering unkind
words about Charlie, Eddie plodded on like a lonely
explorer in the snowy wastes, eventually calling Charlie
all the names of the day. On and on he went, down the
Wee Well Hill, out at the corner on the main road and up
the loanen to big Isaac's house. And when he got there,
puffed out of breath, wasn't the bold Charlie standing at
Big Isaac's with the breadcart intact. Charlie never even
flinched when he got an eyeful of his master and Eddie
stood there and gave Charlie a good telling off in no
uncertain manner. Eddie then went into Big Isaac's with
two loaves and half-a-dozen currant squares and when
Big Isaac heard what had happened he made Eddie a
drop of tea and gave him two of the currant squares. Big
Isaac always had a great fire going in the grate; a mixture
of coal and sticks and, mind you, Eddie was loath to
leave it. But then he began thinking maybe Charlie

would take the rust if left standing out too long and would hive off again in his huff and maybe end up at Sammy Wylie's place away on down the loanen and across the field. So now that the blood was circulating through him as a result of the tea and currant squares and the fire, Eddie went out and took Charlie on to the next call. Big Isaac told him he was lucky having only a few calls to make that evening.

Eddie didn't wish Andy the breadman to hear of his misadventure, and told him that in fact he had sent Charlie on ahead on his own in the snow that day as a test of obedience. Andy told Big Isaac later that he didn't believe that at all, but the incident was soon forgotten.

I used to enjoy Eddie's big white-topped buns when I was sent out to get the bread and I thought it must be great to be a breadman and be able to eat all those lovely buns and cakes when the notion took you. But Eddie told me once that he never ever partook of a bun from the cart while on the rounds. He carried a flask of tea and at certain times of the day stopped and helped himself to a soda farl. I used to think that if I were the breadman there'd be no buns left for the customers at all.

Eddie the breadman was one of the most cheerful men you could have met. Never in all the years that I knew him did I see a frown on his face and he was a friend to all his customers, but then at that time, country breadmen were a race apart. Most of them brought out the newspapers and magazines every week and also the wet wireless batteries after being re-charged in the town. They posted letters, left the orders into the grocers, parcels in the laundry depot, boots and shoes in the cobblers and in addition they carried all the latest news from one district to another.

In outlying districts they were the main link with the outside world. Davy the breadman was a big, gruff countryman who could whistle like a blackbird or thrush and as he jogged along the roads of yesterday, his horse kept tempo to the roll and rhythm of Davy's whistling. You could usually have put on the kettle for the arrival of the breadman and my mother always made a 'squib' of tea with currant squares or Paris buns as a weekly treat. I have heard folks call a cup of tea a 'squig' but my mother maintained it was a 'squib' as her mother before her had called it near Maghery on the shores of Lough Neagh. I never did find out the origins of the name 'squib.' But I do know that a 'squib' tasted better than a sit-down tea at the table – especially when you had a couple of currant squares or Paris buns or big white-topped buns with it.

When the horse breadcart faded out and the motor breadvan took to the roads, the breadman himself didn't change. Some of the older hands retired and others had a difficult time getting used to the comforts of the motor breadvan. One day I asked Eddie what he thought of his new breadvan. 'Ah, it's alright and you don't get any wettings, but at the same time I miss old Charlie, especially on a lovely summer morning along the roads.'

Davy packed in the job when the motorvan arrived and went back to work on the farm, but I have a suspicion that the main reason Davy called it a day when the horse breadcart disappeared was because you just cannot whistle with any feeling or gusto behind a steering wheel instead of atop a cart with the birds joining in the chorus.

The breadman has disappeared from the country roads now. More's the pity. They were part and parcel of the rural picture and the names of the old bakeries are but a memory: McCombs, McWatters, Barney Hughes, and the City Bakery of Armagh. Now the supermarket has taken over and nearly everyone has a car, so the breadman, like the turfman, and the buttermilk man had to move on. But the young fellows in the country these times will never know what it's like to sit up on top of the swaying breadcart and get a run round the roads with genial gentlemen like Eddie.

The barber at the bookies

There are few old-style barber shops in Belfast now and not long ago I heard that there were only about half-a-dozen in all of Dublin's Fair City.

Where would you go now to get a bit of a trim and a shave? The barber's pole is a rare sight these times. The modern salon is not for the older countryman and he would never think of entering the door; in fact he'd rather get a neighbour to put a bowl over his head and get the scissors going. The Lord be with the days when I got a haircut for ninepence (old money that is) with a barber in Armagh who had his shop next door to a bookie's shop. This wee barber was as fast as sheet lightning.

He was fond of putting a couple of bob on the nags and was in and out of the bookies like a yo-yo. When he at last had your haircut finished he always remarked: 'That'll freshen ye up for another while.' He went round heads like a cooper round a barrel. He did a roaring trade on Market Day and on Saturdays, when he'd stay open till ten o'clock at night. He could, as they said, give you a trim while a cat would lick her elbow.

The floor of his shop would be littered with all colours of hair and he never swept it up until closing time. You could have stuffed a mattress with it. A lot of his trade came from the countrymen who came in on bicycles, horse and cart or pony and trap, and on Saturday there'd be maybe a dozen bicycles parked outside the door. John's barber shop was a great meeting place and there was always good crack if you sat and listened to some of the characters. And if you chanced to be a follower of the horses at Sandown or Kempton Park there would be a lot of talk about the gee-gees and what was likely to put up a good show the next day or that evening.

John never wore a barber's apron nor had he the traditional pole outside his premises. He'd say 'Jump into the chair there, ye boy ye and I'll soon take a bit aff it for ye.' And away he'd go with whizzing scissors and clippers; a great barber to go to if you were in a hurry. He was a chain smoker and many a time the ash fell round your head, but John maintained that tobacco ash made your hair grow. There were times however that you could find yourself sitting in the chair for the best part of an hour, as John clipped a swathe, then dashed out with scissors in hand to the bookies to see what won the last race. A terrible man for the horses.

At night after a tiring day, between cutting hair and backing horses, John could be seen heading for a few pints and then away like a hare up the street to the last house of the pictures as he was very fond of a good cowboy film. It used to be in the country that if your hair grew over-long they said you were 'chatin'' the barber. But of course there were some characters so miserable that they wouldn't spend the price of a clip and got a neighbour to do it and mind you when finished they didn't look much like Clark Gable or Robert Taylor at the end. The neighbours were definitely not tonsorial artists. Some men came into John's place and said right off the reel: 'Whack away ye boy ye.'

Barbers such as John are now extinct. More's the pity, for in addition to getting a clip you also had a good bit of crack although at times if John had a couple of winners in a row you were in danger of losing a part of your ear, him being so excited.

Fred's rabbit stew

When Fred the roadman, who lived alone in a labourer's cottage, retired from the council, he spent his time cultivating the best potatoes in the country in his half-acre. They were the envy of all the farmers and were 'Balls of Flour.' When he dug them out in October he stored them carefully in his wee back room and sold the odd stone to eager buyers who even came out of the town for them.

During summer days he spent a lot of time lying in a den in the ditch across the road from his house with a hat half pulled over his eyes. There he took in the passing scene, giving the odd grunt at any passerby in cart, trap, bicycle or on foot. Old Fred wasn't what you'd call a very genial character, but if you knew him well enough you'd find him an interesting man; knowledgable and well read and although he had no wireless set there wasn't much of importance that went on in the world that he wasn't aware of. He had forecast the beginning of the Second World War over a year before it started.

Fred kept his house in order. The labourers' cottages of the thirties and forties were a credit to those who lived in them. They were built of the best material and as sturdy as a rock and some of the survivors today have been sold for thousands of pounds. At the outset the tenant paid a couple of shillings a week in rent and all repairs were carried out promptly and properly by the council of the area. Most of them had lovely little gardens, a blaze of colour in summer days and a lot of tenants like Old Fred grew their own potatoes and vegetables, enough to see them through the year.

Council workers were given priority of tenancy, men like Old Fred and Jack the steamroller man who lived down the road a piece. Fred was a great man with a spade. When he harvested his crop of fine spuds he carefully transferred them to the wee room at the back of the cottage and during a frosty period he covered them with a liberal quantity of straw and a big tarpaulin.

His wages as a roadman might have been £2.10s a week or less when he retired but he could live comfortably and the pipe was never out of his mouth. He got buttermilk from the buttermilk man who passed up the road every Saturday morning. Fred baked good griddle farls and pancakes over his open fire fuelled mainly by sticks cut out of hedges in the vicinity with a slash hook which he would not lend to anyone.

He kept a double-barrelled shotgun and went forth on regular hunting expeditions in pursuit of rabbit, duck or pigeon. He made a lot of rabbit stew in the big pot filled with his homegrown vegetables. As a lad I used to drop into Fred's house and we'd have a yarn and at times he'd be about to have his dinner of rabbit stew. Many a time I sampled it and it tasted good, as did the duck soup. If the day was warm and the broth was hot, Fred used to carry the pot outside and cool it by waving his hat over it backwards and forwards for five minutes.

This venerable old roadman looked out wisely upon the world over his gate or from the den in the ditch during those hazy summer days of fifty years ago.

Jack the roller man

When you were nine or ten the summer holidays from school seemed like an eternity – six weeks of happiness and freedom to roam the fields, meadows and roads. And though they say that there must surely have been rainy days in those far-off Julys and Augusts, I cannot recall a wet day.

The rain went to Spain and didn't show its face again until we returned to school. I got out of bed at seven in the morning, had a hurried breakfast and away with the dogs, Sweeper and Bo. At this time of year along the roads of yesterday the council men were laying down tar with the big steam roller. They spread the tar with large watering-can vessels and my mother would warn me sternly that if a drop of tar got onto my clothes, not all the bleach and soap under the canopy of Heaven would take it off.

The roadmen were a rare breed. Not much crack out of them. Not like the railway permanent way men who laid the sleepers and rails and packed the joints. They were a jolly crew, always whistling and singing. But there was never a cheep out of the roadmen, especially Jack the roller man. He lived in a labourer's cottage with roses round the door at the foot of the Wee Well Hill. After work on a summer evening he'd dander up the road, pipe in mouth and with his hands tucked underneath the back of his coat, he would head for Fred's house for a chat.

When he arrived at Fred's he'd sit down on the green, mossy bank; Fred would come out and together they'd watch the passing scene. Fred was a retired roadman, so they were kindred spirits.

However, when Jack was on the job and standing up in his giant steam roller he would hardly have even noticed Fred. A dedicated roadman and an expert driver of the steam roller; those who knew said he was the best steam roller man in the country.

I had always a great respect for the roller man. Jack was soft-spoken and was never known to raise his voice in anger at anyone – he just kept rolling along with his roller. Jack loved dogs and when he whistled a dog's whistle, all the dogs in the townland came running to him. There were men in the country who had that knack of whistling dogs and their whistle must have had some sort of hypnotic effect on the towsers.

Jack's road roller was a majestic machine. And as it chugged backwards and forwards, bedding down the tar and stones to a fine surface, Jack leaned over the side making sure that every turn of the roller was doing its job. The men who spread the tar wore long, oily aprons and they were bronzed with the summer sun. I used to go down our loanen and watch the roadmen working. I got a ride in Jack's roller a few times and standing there beside Jack, it would have shaken the teeth out of your head as it crawled along, belching smoke.

Like the railwaymen, the roadmen made strong tea in blackened quart cans and sat down on the ditch to enjoy their lunch of a pile of buttered bread and mugs of the tea, and it made you hungry just to watch them. A china cup would have been out of place in the hands of men like Jack the roller man. When the 'new road' was laid it was rough going for a bicycle for the best part of a month, so although it was 'against the law,' you took to the footpath for as far as you could: if there was a footpath that is.

A newly-tarred road had the great aroma on a summer night when Jack the roller man and the others had gone. The grass along the verge or the 'Long Acre' as it was known, would be blackened with the tar and empty tar barrels would be placed here and there in the gaps. When these barrels were emptied, people were allowed to take them, and for years afterwards, many a tar barrel stood under the spout at the gable of the house, catching the rain water. A good tar barrel would last forever, Jack told me once. Jack and Fred cut their own bit of hay for the goats with a scythe and they were both expert scythemen. Jack has long since gone and the big steam roller with him. Resurfacing the roads nowadays doesn't have the same appeal for me.

Johnny the tinman

Long before Judy Garland walked along the Yellow Brick Road to meet the Wizard of Oz, another tinman walked the roads around Armagh City. He was a dapper little man, pleasant of nature who came from the half-door houses of the city's Callan Street, in the thirties, peddling all sorts of tinware; tin cans, tin tea drawers, tin mugs, tin milk cans. They dangled from a strong, thin rope laced over his shoulders and you heard him long before he came into view.

Johnny wore a cap, had puttees wrapped around his ankles and was well liked along the roads. He was no high-powered salesman and if you didn't wish to buy any of his tinware, pleasantries would still flow from him. He never raised his voice and by his manner, anyhow, was a man happy with his lot in life. They said he had soldiered in the Great War but it was a million light years from the fields of Flanders to the quiet little winding roads that ran by the swiftly flowing Callan River which made its never ending journey to the mighty Blackwater, thence to the Bann and into Lough Neagh with all its legends.

Johnny called at our house on the road to Loughgall for years, and early on a Saturday morning you could hear the din of the tins as he came up the loanen from the main road. He'd walk right into the house and sit down, relieving himself of his load of tinware. My mother was of the opinion that tea never tasted better than from a tin mug. Such a mug cost sixpence; a four-pint milk can, a shilling and a tin jug nine pence. Johnny the tinman always got a taste of tea in our house with homemade griddle soda farls baked over the open fire. Of course, he knew everyone in the district and beyond and if someone had fallen ill, had flitted or emigrated, he was the

bearer of the news. That was the time before we got the
wireless set with the wet and dry batteries. That was the
magic box and we listened to the big fights from far away
Madison Square Gardens in New York City, where pugi-
lists such as the great Joe Louis, Max Schmeling, Jack
Dempsey and Billy Conn squared up in the ring.

Anyhow, when Johnny stepped out from Armagh
with his clinking tins slung around him, he was like a
figure who had walked the Yellow Brick Road with
young Dorothy and the others from the other side of the
rainbow. One Saturday morning in early spring Johnny
didn't show up and later we heard the sad news that he
had come to the end of life's road. There was never a
tinman to replace him and from then on if we wanted a
tin utensil I was oftimes despatched to Murphy's the
tinsmith in Armagh where two brothers worked assidu-
ously at their trade. I used to linger long there, watching
them expertly solder the handles of tin mugs with no
apparent effort. The place was coming down with tinware and many a pot, kettle, etc., I brought up on the
bicycle to be repaired. Of course you could have bought a
stopper complete with cork washer to cover the hole in a
bucket or kettle or whatever.

However the tinman was not the only person to walk
the Loughgall Road. Another colourful character was
Jemmy the best nine stone man in the country as he often
exclaimed after a few pints on a Saturday night. He was a
hired man with a farmer and wrought hard all week from
dawn till dusk, but on Saturday evening spruced himself
up and headed off on foot on the four-mile walk to
Armagh where it was his custom to get well inebriated
and come back home on the half-ten bus.

He, too, had soldiered in the Great War and on the
homeward trip always proclaimed on the bus that he had
walked in the footsteps of Our Lord in the Garden of
Gethsemene, a brave step indeed from the townland of
Ballynick. Jemmy was luckier than most hired men in

that the family treated him as one of the family. And even after having a right drop on the night before in a pub called The Garden of Eden, he never missed Mass on a Sunday morning in the little whitewashed chapel of Annacramp. Jemmy was a great attender of wakes and of course in that part of the world at any rate, a wake wouldn't be a wake at all if there wasn't a right drop of drink laid on for the mourners, so Jemmy was always assured of a couple of bottles. He may have walked in the Garden of Gethsemene but as I say, Jemmy never missed a Saturday evening walking up the road to the Garden of Eden. But didn't the poor man deserve his weekly reward and he never said an unkind word about any man, but right to the end maintained that he was the best nine stone man in the country. And who was to dispute that?

Paddy Young was a milestone inspector along the Moy and Loughgall roads in the thirties – a man of the roads that is. He lived in what was little more than a hole in the hedge on the narrow winding road near the site of the Yellow Ford on the Callan River, where 400 and more years ago, Red Hugh O'Neill, Earl of Tyrone among the bushes, fought and defeated the mighty army of Elizabeth the First, led by Marshal Bagenal. Paddy had his 'house' well insulated with straw and hay and when we lads had occasion to pass by, he'd come out and shake a big stick at us and we'd run like rabbits in fear. My father told me that indeed Paddy was a quiet and harmless soul who had once been a schoolmaster away down the country and had taken to the roads for freedom of lifestyle. But us young fellows learned one lesson and that was to keep a safe distance between ourselves and the scowling man with the heavy stick.

Eddie lived on down our loanen and was the Man with a Thousand Watches; big watches, small watches and all sorts of watches. One summer evening he brought out a pile of his watches to the green mossy bank for my inspection. He said he had been collecting these pocket timepieces all his life although he never carried a watch in his own pocket. With bated breath I anticipated the moment when Eddie would say to me: 'Ah well, here's a watch you can have for yourself now.' But it never happened. He said he had hundreds more in the house but I never got the chance of seeing them. When I was ten years old I would loved to have owned a big pocket watch just like the one my Uncle Barney wore in his waistcoat when he came to visit us every August from his home at Columcille on the shores of Lough Neagh. Later, Eddie moved away up the town and I never heard anything more about the watches. Perhaps they are ticking away somewhere today, although Eddie himself has passed from the earthly scene where time doesn't count.

Billy the Fiddler came first to our house one winter night to inspect the new violin my brother John had bought. He was a gruff individual but had the reputation of knowing a lot about fiddles and music, besides being an accomplished player himself. He cycled all over the country to houses where there was a fiddle hanging on the wall. He was said to have had over 2,000 tunes in his head. It was also said that no other fiddler could play 'The Mason's Apron' like Billy could.

The oilcloth man covered the country

The oilcloth man called around our part of the country about three times a year, carrying four rolls of oilcloth and when he called he was always ready for a cup of tea. He was a slight, dapper man who sported a cap on the side of his head and even with his heavy and awkward load perched on his shoulder he seemed to be walking on air as he wore rubber-soled shoes and smoked incessantly.

He was a Portadown man and came up by train. He was a likeable fellow and never tried the hard sell. He was well known along the roads and covered the country around the town. He'd walk into the house and put his load down. Just you try hawking four rolls of oilcloth on your shoulder and I bet you'll feel like partaking of a couple of platefuls of champ before long. Like everything else, the oilcloth man told me once, there was a knack to carrying his rolls. I don't know what profit he made, but he kept coming back, spring, summer, autumn and winter for years during my young days, so he must have been able to make out rightly.

At that time you could have covered your livingroom (or kitchen as it was more often called) for twenty-five or thirty bob. Country folk always liked to have oilcloth as it added lustre to the house and it was easy to keep clean with a wipe of the 'flure cloth.' It was always a pleasant feeling to walk on newly-laid patterned oilcloth, but in winter it was inclined to be 'coul' on the bare feet. Your man was a dab hand at laying it and with a few quick cuts with his knife it fitted like a glove after he had 'stepped' out the area, and most times my mother gave him a couple of bob extra for a packet of Woodbine cigarettes.

In the country at that time carpets were few and far between and only the swanky houses had them. The days of the oilcloth man have passed away like the days of the griddle over the grate.

The house with oilcloth on the floor had usually the man sitting by the fireside smoking a contented pipe and this brings me to the man called Jack who cut his plug tobacco not with a penknife, but with his thumb nail. A small farmer and a cool customer, Jack let the thumb nail of his right hand grow long so that he could cut the tobacco with it. Many a time I watched Jack nail-cutting his tobacco, then rolling it for about five minutes in the palm of his hand, before eventually committing it to his pipe, bedding it carefully in and setting it alight, sending up a cloud of blue smoke. He maintained there was a better flavour of the plug tobacco than the flake or ready rubbed variety and anyhow men like him got added satisfaction from 'manufacturing' it thus. To get plug tobacco going in the pipe takes a certain amount of skill and if the cuts are too big it would take a whole box of matches to get it going. Jack's hard thumb nail never went blunt like a knife.

I haven't seen a man cut tobacco with his thumb nail since Jack. He was also a great conversationalist and could spin a story out of any incident. It was the way he told 'em, you could say.

THE MAN WHO KNEW
EVERYTHING

The constant blast

In the country you will oftimes hear the remark: 'Yer man's not a blow but a constant blast.' To a stranger not of our ways that would seem a puzzling description. A 'blow' is the last type of fellow you would wish to endure for any length of time. He's so full of himself that he'd have you believe he had a Rolls in the garage at home instead of a ribshaker or perhaps a bicycle.

A 'blow' is born and not made and he'll never be anything else. If he hasn't a make in his pocket he'll try to make you believe that he's made of money and a man for all seasons. A 'blow' has been everywhere, seen every-thing and done everything and there is nothing under Heaven that he does not know. In fact he could teach the great philosopher a thing or two and would tell you that Socrates was only a chancer in his day. As time passes the 'blow' becomes known as a 'Constant Blast.'

There is nothing humble about the Constant Blast and although he may live in a humble abode at the back of beyond with hens roosting on the half door, he'll have you believe there's nothing he does not know about computers, spaceflight and what it is like to walk on the moon, though he has never been further than Warren-point, Bangor, Portrush or downtown Richhill. I have known a few Constant Blasts in my time. There is a difference of course in a Constant Blast and a Walter Mitty. The latter lives in a world of his own.

With a know-all grin on his kisser the Constant Blast will stand there leaning over his bicycle at the crossroads and have you believe that his great-great grandmother was a duchess and his great-great-grandfather a Beau Brummel or a tycoon. Without a flinch he'll tell you that he has a right pile of money put away in stocks and bonds and what not, and that he had a wealthy uncle in the oil business in Dallas, Texas, with a place like J. R. Ewing's Southfork. You used to meet the Constant Blast at the dances years ago and he'd ruin your night if you let him. He may be seriously contemplating the purchase of a new car, the latest petrol-drinking model, yet you knew full well that he could hardly buy a new tyre for his bicycle. He might again be thinking of a pricey sports car as he had met this girl in the Charlemont Arms Hotel whose father had a stable of racing thoroughbreds. Not that he wished to make an impression on the bonny lass. Heavens no.

When I was a lad there was a Constant Blast who called regularly at our house. He'd sit there smoking Gallaher Blues and tell about the house he was going to build on a 20 acre site. The same boyo hadn't the grass to graze a goat; in fact the poor oul' dog he had was almost skin and bones and a decent feed would have been the end of it. At times he'd been thinking of purchasing a couple of hundred top Rhode Island Red hens and going into the poultry business – as a sideline. His half-dozen White Wyandottes, had to scrape an existence out of the earth round the house, going back to roost at night half-starved. Then the following night he'd say he was going into pigs.

We were always glad when the Constant Blast got on his bike and headed home. Some people will tell you that you can do your purgatory on earth and listening and enduring a Constant Blast is definitely part of purgatory. If innocently and foolishly enough you chanced to admire his suit he'd turn round and say he was going into town at the weekend to buy a couple of good quality suits for his well stocked wardrobe – not that he needed them of course, for hadn't he a suit for every day of the year and four for a Sunday and Holidays of Obligation, not to mention funeral suits and swallow-tailed jackets and dickey bows and expensive patent shoes for the occasional big ball in Belfast.

We knew that he hadn't even a wardrobe at home and hung his jacket and overcoat on nails behind the door, not that this was anything to be ashamed of, for he wasn't the only one during the thirties with the back of the door for a wardrobe.

However, what cannot be cured must be endured. And as it was then, so it is today. The Constant Blast continues to plague us in the country and we have no alternative but to suffer in silence. After all, aren't we doing our purgatory on earth and won't we get into Heaven all the quicker when we pass on? St Peter, once he hears how we had to endure a Constant Blast on earth will say: 'Ach, come on in, ye boy ye. Ye have earned your reward.'

The man who knew everything

One winter night at the wake of my uncle along the shores of Lough Neagh, I met the man who knew everything. A couple of us had driven through heavy rain and it was midnight when we arrived at the farmhouse. A group of mourners were hunched round the open fire and there parked in the middle of them, was this thin and delicate looking individual, smoking a pipe, which had, he informed his hearers, a rubber shank and mouthpiece: not ordinary rubber which would melt and burn, but a rubber substance just the same. During the course of the night, I had come to the conclusion that I had at last met the man who knew everything.

After we all had tea and cakes and bread, your man lit his rubbery pipe. He was a human encyclopedia and there was nothing under the sun (or above it) he did not profess to know. He could, he said, speak fluently in six languages and there and then gave us a short sample of each. He answered all questions fired at him on medicine, astronomy, anatomy and physiology, mathematics, ancient history, modern history, astrology, psychology, geography, science, theology, architecture, archaeology – and more into the bargain!

He knew everything about printing and literature, and quoted passages from Shakespeare and Shelley, John Donne and W. B. Yeats. He was an expert on cars, airplanes and ships. He had travelled the world and liked Peru best of all. I wondered what a man like him was doing buried here in the boglands around Lough Neagh.

He said that after a couple of years at Queen's University, he left before taking a degree, to work in a chemist's shop in Belfast and cycled 40 miles every morning and every night for years, leaving home at six to start work at nine. He should have been in the Tour of France.

During his time in the chemist's shop he also became a professional embalmer and reeled off the embalmer's formula – formaldehyde and all the mysterious concoctions that went with it. 'A good embalming job makes a corpse twenty years younger looking.'

About three in the morning he started on the Bible, from Genesis right along to the Apocalypse. He had it all off by heart. Did he believe in ghosts? He wasn't too sure about that. But every night for the past 20 years or more he put the tongs on the left hand side of the fire before retiring to bed. And every morning for the same period – when he rose up from the bed he saw that the tongs had been moved to the right hand side of the fire. He was still trying to solve the cause of this phenomenon, but as yet, had reached no satisfactory conclusion.

By six o'clock the cock outside had crowed more than thrice, he was delivering Abraham Lincoln's Gettysburg Address, following up with Robert Emmett's last speech from the dock. By seven, he was reciting Keats' 'Endymion.' After more tea he gave us a lecture on anatomy and we found out that the parietal and occipital bones are in our head and the reason that you can turn your hand almost right round is due to what is called supination of the wrist bones.

That man should have been awarded an honorary doctorate – a special one – which stated he was the man who knew everything.

But the truth was I was glad to see him go home at half-eight. And I wasn't the only one either.

Waterboots and son

The night Dinny's father, known locally as Waterboots, refused to give him the price of the pictures for the third night running, Dinny, who'd have gone any length to see Gary Cooper in a Western, grabbed the hatchet by the fireplace of their humble white-washed abode not a hundred miles from Armagh and made a tear at the oul' lad.

Waterboots, who was every bit as tall as Gary Cooper if he could have got himself straightened up, dashed for the door with pipe still in mouth with Dinny in hot pursuit waving the hatchet like Geronimo. It was a dark winter's night and Waterboots headed like a rabbit hoping to find sanctuary in the home of Willy John, a neighbour who lived his lone on down the loanen. When Waterboots rushed into the house Willy John wondered what in God's name had happened to him as he'd never witnessed him move so spritely before, for a man coming on sixty and plagued with rheumatism.

Waterboots threw himself down on a chair, breathing as if every gasp were his last, telling Willy John how Dinny had lost the bap just because he didn't give him the price of the pictures and anyhow how was he expected to keep Dinny, a grown lad of sixteen, in money for the pictures and Woodbine cigarettes. He wanted to go to the pictures every night and any few bob he earned with the oul' farmer down the road he blew it at the weekend on smokes, fish suppers and film magazines. He was always very pushed to hand Waterboots over a bob or two on Saturday for his keep but expected Waterboots to keep him running to the pictures. Pictures be dammed. They had him the way he was, chasing him with a hatchet thinking he was an Indian or Davy Crockett or somebody. 'Willy John,' says Waterboots,

'I'm goin' up the town to get the police down for that boyo. He should be locked up.'

So Waterboots (who was thus called because all year round he wore nothing but Wellingtons with the tops turned down) headed up the road for the police. An hour later he was back again and planted himself at the foot of the loanen on the main road and him foundered with the cold for it was a hard, black frost the same night. At that time in the thirties, police didn't use squad cars but travelled mostly on bicycles. Two of them landed down, a sergeant and a constable.

'Well,' said the sergeant to Waterboots, 'and where's the bold Dinny boy?' Dinny was no stranger to the lawmen as he had been in the habit of violating one law or another since he was no age, having left school at 12 and refusing to have anything more to do with it. Waterboots told the sergeant he might well be lurking in the house with the hatchet so when they got there, the sergeant and the constable went straight on in without even wiping their feet on the bag at the door.

'Are ye in there Dinny,' cried the sergeant with Waterboots still standing at the door. Dinny wasn't in the house, not even hiding under the bed.

'The bird has flown' said the sergeant solemnly, giving Waterboots an icy look and out they trooped again with their flashlamps shining this way and that and all over the place. They circled the house half-a-dozen times. 'Aye, he's done the bunk,' said the sergeant, 'maybe in the next townland by this time.'

'The divil go with him and I hope he can't find the road back. But what if he does return when you are gone and does me in while I'm sleepin'? The sergeant said that was a chance he'd just have to take. 'Job's Comforter,' whispered Waterboots to himself. On the way past the outhouse, the sergeant's flashlamp caught something behind the big wooden water barrel. 'Ha ha, and what have we here now, I wonder,' he said. The

constable dragged a big tarpaulin from behind the
barrel.

'A tarpaulin of all things,' said the sergeant, 'Very like
the one reported stolen by Jemmy Young's threshing
mill last week. Elementary my dear chaps. Dinny has
pinched Jemmy's tarpaulin and this is it before us.'
Waterboots was no Dr Watson but he guessed the sergeant was right. The sergeant turned his flashlamp on
Waterboot's face. 'Dinny's in trouble now,' he said.

Said the constable flicking through his notebook with
the aid of his flashlamp: 'It's Jemmy Young's tarpaulin all
right, sergeant. I have the full description of the missing
object here. It states there is a considerable sized patch
sewn into one of the corners and there is proof positive as
you can see a similar patch on this tarpaulin.'

'You can dispose of your notebook for the time being,'
said the sergeant sagely. 'What we have to do now is
apprehend the culprit, the bold Dinny himself.' The
tarpaulin was then folded and stashed away in the hedge
to be collected the following morning by a car from the
barracks as it was impossible to convey by bicycle. And
so the police left and Waterboots retired to the couch in
the house and stoked up his pipe again. Since the mother
had passed on there had been no living with Dinny.
Come-easy-go-easy-God-send-Sunday and the pictures
every night with ten Woodbines. He must have intended
to flog the tarpaulin to someone who didn't know it was
stolen property. Well, long runs the fox, thought Waterboots; the tarpaulin could get Dinny locked up in the
Crumlin Road for a spell and there'd be no pictures or
smokes, but a diet of bread and water. It wasn't the first
time Dinny had pinched the odd article here and there
and being a sly one was never caught on, but the tarpaulin could prove his Waterloo.

Once the sergeant got on to anything he'd follow it
through to the bitter end being a dedicated upholder of
the law, something like the policeman in *Les Miserables*

which oddly enough, Dinny had read through when he
was no more than thirteen. Many a night he had read
passages aloud to Waterboots beside the fire when he
was in a good mood and had a packet of fags and the
price of the pictures for the next night or two. Dinny read
a lot of books that Waterboots never heard of and he used
to tell him about the doings of Uriah Heep and Mr
Micawber and the goings on in the Curiosity Shop and a
couple called *Dombey and Son*, places and characters
which held little or no interest for Waterboots for it took
him all his time earning a few bob a week to put a bit of
food on the table and keep the pipe going with Crowbar
Plug tobacco.

As Waterboots sat there in the gloom of a dwindling
fire he began to feel sorry for the son. If the mother had
been spared Dinny might not have been out there in the
darkness and cold, carrying a hatchet and being pursued
by the law. An outcast. Neither food or shelter, and the
winter winds biting into his very bones. And all for the
sake of them Hollywood pictures which were like a drug
to some people these times. Maybe Dinny would come
home during the night. Strangely now Waterboots
didn't feel afraid of him any more. He'd make him a drop
of tea and tell him to go to bed. But then in the morning
the police would be back for the tarpaulin and looking for
Dinny. Waterboots' eyes grew heavy. He put the pipe
aside and fell asleep.

Jacob's Austin 7

Old Jacob punched the day coaxing his handful of hens to lay more eggs, washing the Austin 7 car and endeavouring to beat the bookie and win a few bob on the horses.

After he'd fed the hens in the morning he'd plant himself at the head of the loanen and wait for Black Tam to pass on the bike on his way into town. One day Black Tam had given him a couple of winners at Redcar and since then Jacob would tell you that he was the greatest tipster in the country. However, Black Tam would tell you that old Jacob was the biggest nuisance who ever walked and he often regretted the day he gave him the two horses, which was just pure luck, anyhow.

It was always the same bet with Jacob, one-and-sixpence each way. No danger of him putting his shirt on a horse or gambling himself out of the house. Jacob's missus was a decent soul; she seldom went out of the house and the neighbours called her 'The Cuckoo,' uncharitable people that they were for she was the heart of corn.

The handbrake on the spotlessly clean black Austin 7 wasn't the best and was inclined to slip occasionally. But Jacob always put off taking her into a garage in the town, for he said the garages would rob you. Anyhow he always put her in gear when stationary, so she couldn't run very far. Jacob was a terror for washing and cleaning the Austin 7 down at the quarry hole behind the cottage. The quarry had the reputation of having no bottom to it so none of the locals ever dared swim in it.

On Thursday mornings Jacob and the missus would motor into the town in regal style to collect their pensions. Jacob was like Lord Muck from Clabber Hill; he was a chauffeur in his early days at a big house and one of

the first to drive from Armagh to Dublin, so he looked
the part all right. On Thursday it was straight up to the
post office, collect the pensions, get a few wee odds and
ends, back into the Austin 7 and home again.

On Thursday mornings you wouldn't have known
Jacob at all, for his face was a couple of inches longer and
a good bit thinner, for the false teeth, only worn on this
day, made all the difference. For the rest of the week they
were immersed in a big mug on the dresser beside the
weather cottage.

Every Thursday evening one of us brought him the
local paper from the town and from seven o'clock on he'd
lie back in the rocking chair and make the missus read
out every single line, loud and clear, even the adver-
tisements and especially the auctions for he liked to hear
who was selling and buying land and such.

One Wednesday he ran the Austin 7 down to the
quarry for the weekly wash and spruce-up for the trip on
Thursday for the pension. He parked on an incline as
was his custom, leaving her in gear. He was down at the
quarry for a bucket of water when he heard a voice
calling out to him that the Austin 7 was on the move.
Black Tam roared: 'Hi Jacob, the Austin's heading for the
quarry!' And Jacob or Black Tam couldn't do a thing and
had to watch in horror as she ran on down into the
quarry with no bottom in it. Soon all Jacob could see was
the disappearing back number plate and bumper. Black
Tam tried to console him by saying he was lucky he
wasn't in her, when she went down like the Titanic.

The fire brigade was summoned and the Austin 7 was
retrieved but it took six months (all that summer and
more) to dry her out. When she was roadworthy again
Jacob sold her. He never backed another horse and as
time went on the hens grew thinner and thinner and
stopped laying and Jacob sold them to a hook of a
fowlman who diddled him in the price. Afterwards,
Jacob and his missus went into the town each Thursday

by bus to collect their pensions. Soon he went alone to collect both, telling Black Tam there wasn't much sense in the two of them paying bus fares. Then he stopped getting the weekly paper and the missus sighed with relief. They say he never went down near the quarry hole again.

Bannocky Bill and Reuben

Bannocky Bill was a wee wisp of a man hired, for his keep and an ounce of pipe tobacco weekly, by two bachelor brothers, Joe and Daniel who had a right big farm. Bannocky Bill had always a crabbit face on him and no wonder, for he was worked harder than the horses from daylight to long after dark, right through the year, never knowing what it was to sit back and put his feet up. Locals said he seen more dinner-times than dinners, but I wouldn't go as far as saying that, for many a time I was in the same house and the grub looked wholesome enough, it being in the thirties. Plain and wholesome grub it was; plenty of homemade bread, stirabout morning and night, good churned butter and a copious supply of fresh buttermilk.

Resting on the Sabbath might have been something Bannocky Bill read about in the Bible. Come day, go day, God send Sunday meant little to him, for every day and every night was the same.

Reuben wrought with Bannocky Bill and was cast in a similar mould. Can you imagine a hired man called Reuben? He was a great grafter and work was his life, even though he had no choice in the matter. He smoked a pipe with half a mouthpiece on it and watching Reuben fill that pipe was an education. He'd cut a whack of the plug of tobacco and then grind it in the palm of one hand until correctly processed. Then he'd pack it deftly into the pipe never dropping a shred of the precious weed for indeed that plug would probably have to last for a week.

Bannocky Bill didn't smoke as much as Reuben, with the result that Reuben was regularly tapping him for a fill and then Bannocky would let out a stream of curses at Reuben and maybe make for him with the graip or pitchfork or whatever implement was in close proximity.

Bannocky continually chewed corn and wheat and always carried a plentiful supply around with him in his pockets. During the course of a year he must have gone through a hundredweight of grain and I often thought it a wonder the two oul' brothers didn't moan about the loss of their corn and wheat, for the same two were so miserly they shared the one set of false teeth between them. Hard to believe, perhaps, but it was true. They didn't wear them about the home place, but on market day which was a Tuesday, they took turns in going into town to the market, either with the horse and cart or pony and trap and when they did so they put in the teeth and so it went on, going to market and wearing the false teeth on alternate Tuesdays.

Bannocky Bill drove the farmers' pony and small flat cart with rubber wheels forever up and down the very steep hill, criss-crossing it via the well worn cart track. The poor pony got to the stage of being broken-winded and one day when Bannocky was in the town with a load of spuds, didn't somebody tell him to get a bottle of smelling salts in the chemists, saying that an odd whiff of the same would add life to the pony when it started wheezing and coughing.

So Bannocky got the smelling salts and for a long time afterwards when the pony would start the wheezing, Bannocky would stop, take out the smelling salts and give it a whiff or two and he would scarcely have time to get aboard the cart again, for the pony would throw up its tail and go off like a whippet, up the steep hill.

Reuben had a fearsome looking moustache with eyes like Christopher Lee in one of those horror films and when I was young I was afraid of him to put it mildly, but there was no harm in the man at all. Bannocky Bill came down the hill of an odd winter night to make his ceilidhe in our house. The two brothers didn't like the idea of their workers finding time to make their ceilidhe, so as I say, they were odd occasions.

My father always saw to it that he got a mugful of tea and as much bread and butter and jam as he could consume for he was fond of Bannocky and Reuben too. Bannocky would relish sitting beside the fire, smoking a contented pipe and telling stories about the time long, long before when he was young and running the country.

Reuben on the other hand wasn't the sociable sort at all. He was an awful coward after dark, although to look at him you'd think him fearless. And I vividly remember the November night when Young Jim (the neighbour who had a thousand watches) scared the life out of him. Young Jim got a white sheet off the bed, draped it over himself and sat on the cart track halfway up the steep hill. When Reuben, who could have been doing with a whiff of smelling salts at times himself, came to the spot and saw the ghost he let out a yell that brought half the district to the door. Young Jim, sheet and all, jumped up and chased poor Reuben right on up the hill and right round the haggard of the farmhouse and Reuben nearly took the door with him on the way into the house. And it was said that he refused to get out of bed the next morning, being petrified, and didn't rise until dinner-time and the two brothers thought maybe he was going to die and kept him indoors for the rest of the day, making him take platefuls of hot soup and spuds to get his strength back, for the work just couldn't wait too long on Reuben getting better.

There are no men on the land nowadays like Bannocky Bill and Reuben; simple hard-working men who wrought for their keep and a bit of tobacco. On reflection they were like two figures out of the Old Testament. They must surely be in Heaven this night and at peace after their long, hard pilgrimage through the Valley of Tears.

Joe the Nettle Strapper

Years ago in the town of Newry I got to hear of Joe the Nettle Strapper. Now you can consult all the dictionaries you like but you'll not come across the definition of a Nettle Strapper. Anyhow, in a Newry townland, Joe was well known and highly respected and when men met him on the road they raised their hats and caps to him like they would to a clergyman or a doctor. You see, he was something of a man of medicine, although he hadn't any medical degrees or such. But he had a cure and that to the people of the area was far more important than having a string of letters after his name.

Joe the Nettle Strapper was a tall man with not a pick on him and he wore a long coat that almost trailed the ground and sported a big felt hat nearly covering his eyes, something like Clint Eastwood the Hollywood actor in one of those Spaghetti Westerns. His services were often called upon and he travelled over a wide area to carry out his cure. He specialised in the treatment of pains, such as a sore back, a sore leg or the like.

He didn't prescribe pills or bottles of homemade medicine and his brand of treatment had a sting in it, to put it mildly. He used the Nettle Treatment which was then and despite the progress of medical science, still is, unknown to the doctors of Ireland. When called upon to exercise his curative skills, Joe, an eccentric character at the best of times, arrived at the patient's house, carrying a big bundle of nettles neatly tied together. All fresh, mature nettles they were, plucked at dawn when the dew was still on them.

Entering the patient's home, he would proceed to take off his heavy overcoat and hat and then without further ado, direct the 'victim' to lie down on the couch or bed, or even the floor, and take his shirt off, or if their leg was

79

giving the trouble, the trousers. Then Joe, spitting on his hands, like a man about to dig a ditch, or cut a hedge, would set about flailing the poor unfortunate patient with the bundle of nettles until his body was a mass of red, blistery lumps and him stung to the bone. Talk about bitter medicine!

The Nettle Strapping treatment might last for a good ten minutes or more and then Joe would step back, tell your man to gather himself up and put on his shirt or trousers, assuring him that never again would he feel even a twinge of his old painful affliction, whether it was rheumatism, lumbago, sciatica, or whatever.

True enough I was told by a man who received the Nettle Treatment, that for years he was full of pains in body and legs and after Joe had finished with him, he said he felt a new man entirely, although he admitted it was a day or two before he got rid of the 'side effects' of the cure.

I was told it was best to ask Joe for his cure in the spring or early summer for it is then that the nettle is at its best. Come winter it has lost most of its curative values, but apparently he was so good at his job, he could and did take on cases even on Christmas Day or New Year's Day, when the nettle has barely a sting left.

A certain man in the same district once managed to bottle the juice of nettles and gave it to a neighbour in an effort to cure his sore back. But didn't it almost poison the poor fellow and he turned a greenish colour and only the doctor came out and prescribed a strong dose of Epsom Salts, he'd have been a goner.

I told some of the men around my own district of Armagh about Joe the Nettle Strapper and some of them went off right away to see him, but he must have been an elusive character, for they couldn't track him down and they came home in worse shape than ever.

Bob the ploughman was plagued with pains in the legs and was finding it difficult to follow a pair of horses in the field, so one evening, Fred the roadman, who spent most of the summer nights lying on the roadside by his labourer's cottage, went off and gathered a big pile of nettles. When Bob called that night for the usual game of cards with a couple of other mates, Fred told him to drop the trousers and he'd soon put him on his feet again. But Bob took a look at him and the bunch of nettles and says he to Fred: 'Are ye feelin' all right, ye oul' eejit ye!' and limped out of the house and away down the road, thinking sure that Fred had lost the bap altogether.

I remember in the early forties there was a man down our road who had the cure for the nose bleed. One night my mother's nose began to bleed rather badly and I was told to jump on the bicycle and away with me to the man with the cure. It was exactly seven o'clock when I left home and I arrived at the house at half-past seven. I knocked the door and your man, a quiet, respectable businessman in Armagh, he was, came out and asked me what was the matter, so I explained about my mother's nose bleed. He asked me what time it had started and I told him. He then told me to go on back home and everything would be fine. I half expected him to give me something or other for the cure, but he just said 'Goodnight' and closed the door.

When I arrived back home the bleeding had completely stopped. I asked what time it had ceased and my mother said exactly half-past seven, the time when the man with the cure had told me everything would be all right. She never had a nose bleed afterwards.

Again I recall when I was about seventeen years old and had about eight ugly warts on the back of my left hand, not a pretty sight when you're running the country dancing. I had tried lots of remedies from both doctor and chemist, but all to no avail. Then up the town one night I was told to go up to a Mrs. . . . . McK. . . . . in the city's Upper Irish Street who had the cure or charm for warts. Not expecting any miracles I headed for the good woman's house. She ushered me into a room, sat on a chair beside me and began to count my warts. That was all. It didn't take a minute or two. Then she got up and showed me to the door and told me all would be well. Again there was no medicine or concoction of any kind. When I awoke the following morning the ugly warts had vanished. So to this day don't tell me that charms are all whigmaleery!

The library meeting

Every time I hear of elections of any sort I right away think of the time I was elected the official 'Book Stamper' for our little church library at Annacramp between Armagh and Loughgall. The inaugural meeting was held one wild wintry night in a cottage near the Callan River. This was a very memorable meeting and I got such a sickener of the whole carry-on, I vowed I'd never put a foot at another meeting, no matter what.

There was the motor mechanic Barney, a quiet and decent big fellow who came out of Banbrook School in the thirties with the reputation of being a 'good scholar'; Joe, who was a great man for going to the dances all over the country; pipe-smoking Jack, a small farmer and something of a philosopher; the sisters Agnes and Bridget, two quiet, decent ladies; and myself.

The self-appointed chairman of the library committee was the brains behind it all. He looked every inch like one of those eccentric professors, sporting a trim, goat-like beard, a mop of silver hair (he'd cheated the barber, Barney said) and he wore heavy Donegal tweeds. He was a colourful character and travelled in and out of Armagh City on the bicycle and the way he perched straight up in the saddle, you'd have thought he was about to take off over Beecher's Brook. I'll call him the Professor.

He always had a big knapsack on his back and it was a constant mystery to one and all as to what he carried in it up and down the road. He was the sort of individual who could hardly give you a straight answer if it was to save his life. But everyone was unanimous that he was a very brainy man and don't they say that these intellectuals can be an odd lot anyhow. To digress momentarily from the inaugural meeting of the library. One day the Professor was riding up the road with his knapsack on his

back and one of the lads spotted him and popped in
behind the ditch and started to shout 'Oul' stiff legs' at
him. The Professor jumped briskly off the bike and
literally danced in the middle of the road with uncon-
trollable rage. But your man behind the ditch kept shouting 'Oul' stiff legs' and began to fling big sods over the
hedge at him.

The Professor made it known to his unseen attacker
that his first call in the town would be at the police
barracks to report the sordid affair when he would tell
how his free passage on the public highway had been
obstructed by some uncouth gulpen. But if the police did
come out that day, your man wasn't behind the ditch
when they arrived and that was that.

So back to the library meeting on that inclement
winter's night, 'not a fit night out for man or beast' as W.
C. Fields would have put it. When Barney and myself got
to the house on the bikes we were wringing wet. 'It's
exactly two-and-a-half minutes after eight' said the Professor 'and the meeting was convened for eight o'clock.'
Joe, Jack, Agnes and Bridget were on time but they
hadn't all that far to travel, just down the lane apiece.
Then the Professor struck the big round oak table with
his gavel and summoned the meeting to order.

There we were sitting like Knights of the Round Table
and Barney and me with the water dripping down our
legs into our boots. The Professor arose and as if he were
addressing the House of Lords, with the thumb of his
right hand tucked underneath the armpit of his waistcoat
and his left hand resting on a large volume on the table,
asked us if we ever wondered how a spider went about
spinning its web. Joe squinted over at Jack. 'What had
oul' spiders to do with starting up a small library?,' I
wondered. There and then we were given a lecture on a
day in the life of a spider with emphasis on its inherent
skill as a web winder. He then moved from spiders to
butterflies.

Barney, now getting rather restless, wet and uncomfortable, gave me the odd dig in the ribs with his elbow
and by now the water running from our clothing was
forming a little pool on the floor. The Professor took a
long, hard look at each of us in turn, in the process of
which Jack's pipe went out and he was reticent about
striking a match to get it going again. 'I'm wondering'
said the Professor, 'just what qualities you people
have in order to make up a library committee? You,
(pointing a long lean finger at me) have you read *The Rise
and Fall of the Roman Empire* or Paine's *The Rights of
Man?*

I told him honestly that I'd read *Under Western Stars* by
Zane Gray and *The Adventures of Tarzan and Cheetah* and
Huckleberry Finn and that I had also seen the film of the
latter story with Mickey Rooney as Huck Finn. Barney
confessed he read little except the *Belfast Telegraph* and
Irish News. Jack had read *Decline and Fall,* Joe couldn't
remember ever having read it and Agnes and Bridget
admitted they preferred romantic stories. Summing up,
The Professor advised us all to read at our earliest con-
venience *My New Curate* by Canon Sheehan and the
poems of W. B. Yeats and Ezra Pound. Following this he
rendered a fifteen-minute lecture on the progress of
literature from Chaucer's *Canterbury Tales* to Dickens and
Thackeray and Gerard Manley Hoplins, not forgetting
Socrates, Plato and Wordsworth, Shelly and Keats.

Well, it was all as I roved out to those assembled,
especially Barney and myself but we nodded and
listened as the great man rambled away. It wouldn't
have been half as bad if we hadn't been wringing wet.
Round the walls of the comfortable room there were
large maps and big pictures of Rommel, Montgomery
and Churchill. Those three, he pointed out were men of
great integrity and an example for us all. I had seen
pictures of Field Marshal Rommel in the Pathe Newsreel
in the Cosy Corner Picture House, as had Barney and we

didn't think all that much of him. In fact, to us he was a bit like his boss Hitler during the war.

How are ye, Burke, says I to myself, this man is a bloody marvel. And then I remembered the chap who had fired big sods at the Professor along the road and called him 'Oul' stiff legs' and it took me all my time to refrain from loud laughter and mind you, it's hard to laugh when you're wringing wet and your feet are in gullion, as my mother used to say if your feet got wet.

At long last, two hours later, the Professor appointed himself library committee chairman and I was elected Stamper of Books. The others were elected to various jobs. I was ceremoniously presented with the date stamper and stamp pad. The new library would open at Annacramp after Mass the following Sunday. There were a dozen or two books in stock, including *Northern Iron* by George A. Birmingham, *Dan the dollar*, *Knocknagow – or The homes of Tipperary* by Charles Kickham and *My new curate* by Canon Sheehan.

That was that. Barney and I went home on our bikes, still wet and uncomfortable but now the rain was over and a soft breeze was drying us out as we went along. We went home that night knowing more about spiders' webs, butterflies and General Rommel than we did about the functions of a small parish library. The library lasted for quite a spell, although Barney dropped out of the committee. Each Sunday morning I really enjoyed stamping out the books. Looking back now the Professor was quite a wonderful character who took the whole thing very seriously and was forever changing the stock of books. He must have read every book ever printed. There were times later when I'd be talking with him and I saw the other side of his character – a gentle, kind and understanding part of him. You know, every time I think of him now I right away think of George Bernard Shaw.

AND THE BAND PLAYED ON

Love's labour lost

All the world, they say, loves a lover, but at times up-the-country in the forties when we were all dancing mad and never out of the picture houses, the real life love story didn't always work out to the satisfaction of both parties.

I once found myself playing the unlikely role of match-maker to what I thought was the blossoming of young love under the moon in June and all that. There were these two lads, both good friends of mine, Charlie and John who had the same surname, apart from which they had very little else in common. Charlie, a studious chap with a good head on him, loved classical music, Beethoven and Chopin and all that jazz and he was forever thumping out Wagner and Schubert and such on the old ivory keys in his home in the town. He was good at it too, or so he said anyhow and we had to take his word for it, for the other lads and myself didn't know much if anything about these composers with strange sounding names and we'd have preferred to listen to Joe Loss playing 'In the Mood.'

John worked on the railway – the old Great Northern Railway that is, at Portadown station (then known as the Crewe of the North on account of it being the busiest rail junction in the north of Ireland) – lived four miles out of Armagh in the vicinity of Richhill; rode a nice Raleigh bicycle and scraped a bit on the fiddle – his repertoire consisting of three pieces, 'Kitty of Coleraine,' 'Danny Boy' and 'Did Your Mother Come From Ireland.' To John who smoked 'Players Please' cigarettes to the band playing, Beethoven and Wagner and Chopin and Liszt were just vague foreign characters who lived hundreds of years back. Their music was never heard at Ballycrummy dance hall, better known as Tintown, on account of it being constructed with tin or zinc. Of course Charlie never darkened the door of Tintown, but never missed the celebrity concerts held at intervals in the City Hall. John wouldn't have gone there if they had paid him to go and that went for the rest of us also.

Now enter the fair Molly, a red-cheeked colleen who might well have stepped out of an Irish picture postcard so beloved by our American cousins who also believe in fairies and such. Anyhow, one night I'm stepping out along the road in the direction of the Cosy Corner Picture Palace to see Johnny Mack Brown in a cowboy film called 'Shoot-out at Gunsight Pass,' when who did I meet but the fair lass Molly on her bicycle.

'Here,' says she, 'will you put in a good word for me with your man O'Shaughnessy? He's a lovely fella and I'd love a date with him and walk arm in arm together down Mullinure Loanen. And I know too that he's a powerful good musician and I love music. Will you try and fix me up?'

'It's as good as done, Molly asthore,' says I right up to her. 'Leave the details to me. You're as good as in Mullinure Loanen with him now.'

Off she went as happy as a lark, singing 'When You and I Were Young, Maggie.' Would you credit that, says I to myself. I'd never have thought merry Molly liked this classical music, but doesn't it take all sorts? A couple of days later I hear that Molly is in hospital with a touch of pleurisy or something and doesn't she send me a special messenger with a note saying she'd get better immediately if I could manage to bring your man O'Shaughnessy up to visit her in hospital. Fair enough, says I to myself. That evening I make it my business to call at Charlie's house and tell him how poor sick Molly was longing to see him and wouldn't it be a shame if he didn't go to see her and maybe bring her some sweets.

Charlie was in the middle of a Rimsky-Korsakoff medley when I got there and his hands were flying over the keys in wild abandon. He should certainly be able to play the Irish reel 'The Pigeon on the Gate,' I thought, knowing of course that such was an anathema to him. I informed him that the fair Molly from Allistragh direction had a powerful notion of him and had asked me to fix it up for her and that in fact the poor lass was at that moment lying in her sick bed up in the hospital, and wanted him to go and visit her. 'Well, well,' said Charlie, swinging round on the piano stool, 'what do you think of that?' He confessed there and then to my utter surprise in fact that for quite some period of time he had had a right strong notion of Molly, for of course, he knew her to see passing by on her bike.

The following night as the stars dazzled from a clear blue sky, Charlie and I headed for the hospital. He was carrying a box of chocolates and big bunch of flowers. Into the ward we go and over to Molly's bedside. Without further ado, says I to Molly, 'Well, Molly, here's Charlie.' Molly was looking terrible well and had dolled herself up just in case O'Shaughnessy would breeze in. Well, she propped herself up in the bed and gave me a look and then gives Charlie a look. Charlie was a man for all seasons and after he had handed over the chocolates and flowers, shook Molly by the hand. His face had lit up, but I noticed that Molly's had dropped somewhat. Charlie started the old conversation with Molly, pulling up a chair as if he were at home or sitting down to play some Chopin.

I cut my stick and went out, for the strange thing is that when I have occasion to visit anyone in hospital, which is not too often if I can prevent it, I am always dying for a smoke the minute I go in. I sat on the wall outside and puffed five or six fags. Then Charlie appeared. Looking a trifle mystified he said that Molly wished to see me for a minute. I'm a little puzzled myself as I go in, snigging my butt at the door.

I thought at first that poor Molly had taken a sudden turn for the worse. She looked rather sad.

Says she rather brazenly: 'And who was that you brought in to see me, tell me?' 'That was Charlie O'Shaughnessy whom you told me you had a notion of. D'ye not mind?' Lord maybe she was running a fever, I thought.

Gobbling a few chocolates she said: 'I know that was Charlie O'Shaughnessy, but I didn't want to see him. I meant John O'Shaughnessy, the fella with the sports coat, the Raleigh bike, the crease in his trousers and who plays the fiddle.'

Poor Molly looked forlorn. I had brought the wrong O'Shaughnessy and felt like a right charlie. 'There he was,' exclaimed Molly, 'talking about us walking down Mullinure Loanen under the moon and stars and us holding hands. You know I looked at him not knowing what to say. I felt like hiding under the bedclothes. Didn't ye know it was John I wanted to meet. Oh Lord if it had only been John who came to visit me here tonight I'd have jumped out of this bed and went off with him on the bike, anywhere!'

Well, you see the whole mix-up was on account of music – and a mixture of Mozart, 'Danny Boy,' Beethoven and 'Did Your Mother Come From Ireland?' When Molly got well again, she never did go walking down Mullinure Loanen. About a week later, John packed his bags and his fiddle and took the boat for London and I didn't hear from him since, for over 40 years, would you believe it. And Charlie went back to Wagner and Beethoven. He asked me why Molly wanted to see me that night at the hospital and I had to tell him a barefaced lie, the Lord forgive me. I had to tell him that she was too shy to say much when he visited her but that she'd see him out and about shortly. But they never did meet again and for a while poor Molly was heartbroken on account of John taking the boat. As for John, he never knew that Molly had a notion of him. I intended to tell him, but he was off to London before I got the chance.

Aye, Shakespeare must have been right. The course of true love never does run smooth. I got the whole thing out of my mind by going to the Cosy Corner Picture Palace and the City Cinema every night for a fortnight. Why couldn't I be like George Raft or James Cagney or Edward G. Robinson? They'd never set themselves up as matchmakers, would they?

They don't go walking down Lover's Lane

Time was in the country if a chap was 'going strong,' there wasn't many who didn't know about it and around the fire, in the fields and at the crossroads, it usually crept into the conversation. John and Maggie might not have been aware of it but if, perchance, their ears were warm on occasions, this was the reason why.

The fellow who was going strong might as well have been married, for he dare hardly stop to have a word with another girl and if he did and was spotted then the tongues would start to wag overtime. And the same went for Maggie. She daren't even glance or smile at another chap and if she did she might as well have put it in the local paper.

Many a time in the early forties when I'd be loitering at the corner with a few chaps, John might pass on the bike and someone in the assembly would say: 'Ye know yer man John there is goin' strong. If he's not going' to see yer woman then he must be layin' away.'

'Laying away' meant that a fellow who was doing a strong line with a girl was seeing another lass on the quiet; just like the hen sneaking off to lay her eggs under a hedge. Mind you quite a few of the lads who were going strong were also laying away. You couldn't miss but notice it at a dance, for instance. You knew fine well, like most others did that Albert was going strong with Big Aggie, but here he was at the dance stepping it out all night with another dilcy. And he was barefaced too about it. And you'd have to admit that Albert was a man of much courage for as sure as the sun would come up the next morning, Big Aggie was bound to get to hear of it, but then I suppose Albert would swear it was all a tissue of lies.

Going strong also meant that a fellow had got his legs

93

under the table of the girl's house, being invited in for tea and wee buns or homemade pancakes. Once you got your feet under the table it was difficult to have a free footing again. That was one of the perils. And again when the oul' dog at the girl's home stopped barking at you this was another sign that you were well on the way to being nabbed. Many a chap who found himself going strong lived to regret it and oftimes at the heels of the hunt it led to the altar even though your man had never any notion of walking down the aisle and all that.

However, I knew a lot of couples who were going strong for years but never got officially engaged, but then years ago in rural parts at any rate, this business of buying the lass an engagement ring was not a common practice mainly because the lads thought it a great waste of hard come by money to buy such a ring, which to them didn't mean much, anyhow. The only one to whom it did mean much was the oul' lad in the jeweller's shop who, as they say, saw them coming.

Times have certainly changed and you see girls in their teens flashing expensive engagement rings which might cost your man a couple of hundred quid, someone with more money than sense, do I hear you say? The same boy mightn't have a shoe on his foot or a dacent stitch on his back. I knew one fellow who went strong with a girl for 25 years. The oul' dog had not only stopped barking at him but its pups and their pups and their pups had long since passed away to the place where good dogs go.

There were the wise men and women in the country who said: 'Ah, there's Jack and Biddy. They've been going strong for many a year. A quare sensible pair they are too. Ye never see one without the other. A quare sensible couple.' Did they call them the quare sensible pair because they never got married? But then didn't St Paul say somewhere it was better to marry than to be burned? That one is hard to fathom and maybe Paul was just codding at the time.

Despite the song there was very little courting in the kitchen and most of it was behind the ditches, especially on a summer night along Lover's Lane. There were a lot of lover's lanes dotted here and there and the famous one round Armagh was Mullinure Loanen, where there was a courting den every 20 yards and you'd have tripped over the couples if you were a stranger walking that way. Mullinure Loanen was the road of romance, an idyllic place under the moon in June and all that. The lark sang there in summer and the corncrake was heard at day's end along the big meadow where the aroma of new mown hay wafted, as Stephen C. Foster wrote . . . 'on the soft summer air . . .' Couples who were going strong frequented Mullinure Loanen as regulars.

These times the ways of courting couples have changed and no more do they walk along lover's lanes under the young May moon. They're sitting in either her house or his house watching television and the oul' pair are sitting there too. And if they're not there they're sitting in some of these lounge bars sipping drinks. What has happened to romance at all? Forty years ago if you had a date with a girl you agreed on a place along the road to meet, or being bolder, ventured to within whistling distance of the house. Most times, I suppose, the oul' pair would be watching out behind the curtains and say to the daughter: 'There's that boyo whistling for ye again. Ye better watch yerself there. I don't like the way he whistles. Wouldn't ye think he was whistlin' an' oul' dog. He's worth a-watchin' now . . .'

God help their wit anyhow for the girl took little notice of their wise remarks and sallied forth and maybe got on the bar of yer man's bicycle and away with them to the likes of Mullinure Loanen. And wasn't that real rural romance?

Of course there were the lads who were called 'Duffy's Circus' with a girl – one night only. But they were harmless, for youth must have its fling and if they're still to the fore these times, sure they're oul' folk, not fit to ride a bicycle, never mind court along Mullinure Loanen. They sit in the ashes watching television and do nothing but ridicule the young ones saying they were never like that in their day. Oul' hypocrites. But sure that's the way of the world.

Nights at the Cosy Corner

Being a very keen picturegoer through the forties, I still have a diary for 1943 in which I have duly entered all the movies I saw during that year when I was seventeen, going on eighteen. It is the only diary I have ever completed and flicking through the pages now brings me back to the good old days when I went to all the films in Armagh's three picture houses, The City Cinema, The Cosy Corner and The Ritz.

There were at least two 'changes' in each every week so I sat through a lot of pictures, enjoying every one. On Saturday March 20 I saw 'Mrs Miniver' starring Walter Pidgeon and Greer Garson in The City Cinema where you got into the body of the cinema for ninepence and the 'dear' part at the back, on a slightly higher level, for one shilling and three pence.

And then on March 26 I went along to the Tramps' Ball in the City Hall, when as far as I can remember, quite a lot dressed up for the occasion. During the forties, I was also an avid dancer you see; never a Fred Astaire mind you, but like most other young fellows fond of shaking a leg in halls all over the place, the main one being the grand City Hall in Armagh, now alas no more.

Going to the pictures and going to the dances – that was our way of life and very few frequented pubs, and of course lounge bars and pub enterainment were still a long way off. So you headed off to the last house of the movies with a packet of Woodbine cigarettes and a bar of toffee. From 1940 onwards I bought two weekly film magazines, *Picturegoer* and *Film Weekly*, and I knew every actor in Hollywood, every director, every producer etc, etc, etc.

By 1941 I had a grand collection of film star photographs sent to me from Hollywood, California. I wrote to all my favourite stars; Gary Cooper, Clark Gable, Robert Taylor, Lloyd Nolan, Joel McCrea, Spencer Tracey, George Raft – and of course the girl with the most glorious voice in the world, the lovely Deanna Durbin. I received a nice letter from young Mickey Rooney with his glossy picture, informing me that he and Judy Garland had just finished making 'Strike up the Band.'

But away from Hollywood briefly, for there in my diary for Friday April 2 of 1943, I was in the picture with Cardinal Spellman of New York (then Bishop) outside St Patrick's Cathedral, Armagh on the occasion of his visit to Cardinal MacRory.

Back to Sunday January 3 I was at a dance in the Grange, a little Hibernian hall outside Armagh near the Yellow Ford on the Callan River. And when the dance was over I went to Barney Coey's wedding party, where I was called upon to supply the music for a hooley in the kitchen, on a violin. The cow calved during the celebrations and we all adjourned to the byre, where the dance continued. Aye, lost chords, where are they?

On January 4 I received a photograph from Hopalong Cassidy (Bill Boyd) the famous cowboy. When John the postman brought each big envelope with Paramount Studios, Burbank, California stamped large, he used to ask my mother how in Heaven's name I got to know all these film stars!

Anyhow, here's a list of the January movies of '43. 'Wake up and Dream,' 'The Goose steps out,' 'Miss Annie Rooney,' 'The Wolf Man,' 'Here comes Mr Jordan' starring Robert Montgomery; 'Kid Glove Killer,' 'Man at large,' 'Hellzapoppin,' 'Great guns' (the great Laurel and Hardy); 'Louisiana Purchase' (Bob Hope), 'Three Girls about Town,' 'Three Yanks in Trinidad.'

On January 15, our dog Shep had pups, an event which did not deter me from attending a ceili in the City Hall that night.

Some of the February movies were 'Babes on

Broadway' with Mickey Rooney; 'China seas', 'Dangerously they lived,' 'Pardon my sarong,' 'Jungle Man' 'North to the Klondike,' 'Eagle Squadron,' 'Ship ahoy,' 'Born to Sing,' 'Texas,' 'Andy Hardy's Courtship' (Mickey Rooney) one of the then famous Andy Hardy series.

On February 10 I joined the Armagh City Harriers and 'ran out the Moy Road.' On March 5 I saw 'Flight Lieutenant' in the Cosy Corner and then went to a dance in the Asylum, now St Luke's Psychiatric Hospital, Armagh. My mother used to say I would need my head examined on account of running to so many dances and pictures, but the dances held regularly in the hospital were very enjoyable and you had to procure an invitation or 'invite' as we called it then to gain admission.

On Sunday March 14 I was dancing, the following night I was attending a Pioneer meeting in Annacramp Chapel and on Tuesday night I was at the Ritz watching 'Somewhere I'll Find You.' Weren't Clark Gable and Lana Turner in that one? On Wednesday night I was dancing again in the Grange at a half night; on Thursday I went to 'Man with two Lives'; on Friday night it was 'I met my Love Again' and on the Saturday night to the famous 'Mrs Miniver.'

April – scared going home after watching 'Ghost of Frankenstein' with the great Boris Karloff. Still vividly remember Tracey and Gable in 'San Francisco.' Anyone recall a move called 'Affairs of Jimmy Valentine?' There were, among others, 'Always in my Heart,' 'Stick to your Guns,' 'Jackass Mail,' The Remarkable Andrew,' 'Raiders of the Desert.' The following night it is recorded 'I lost my bicycle.' In other words it had been pinched from McStravick's Yard in Armagh when I had been at the pictures watching 'They Died with their Boots On,' starring Errol Flynn.

May brought 'Crossroads,' 'Variety on Parade,' 'A Yank at Eton,' 'Bambi,' 'Reap the Wild Wind' (Ray Mill-

and), 'Her Cardboard Lover,' 'No Hands on the Clock,' 'Submarine Raider,' 'Old Mother Riley M.P.' I had also recorded in my diary that on May 19, I attended the inaugural meeting for the formation of Annacramp Chapel library in Paddy Donnelly's house at the Grange and was appointed official book stamper. Dancing every Sunday night as usual with a big dance in the City Hall on Wednesday 26. The next evening I was throwing bullets (road bowls on the Loughgall Road). Missed the movies that night. The following Sunday night I was at a fun fair at the Christian Brothers' School.

From then through to November of the year 1943, my diary records scores of pictures and as many dances, but suffice to mention but a few movies. There was 'Beyond the Blue Horizon,' 'Arabian Nights,' 'Across the Pacific' with Humphrey Bogart, 'The Man who Returned to Life,' 'Seven Sisters' (Van Heflin, he of the famous Western 'Shane'), 'Money for Jam,' 'How Green was My Valley' (Walter Pidgeon, fine actor), 'The Falcon's Brother,' 'Baby-Face Morgan,' 'Johnny Comes Marching Home,' 'Desperadoes' (Randolph Scott), 'Tombstone' (Richard Dix), 'Love Affair' (Charles Boyer – never one of my favourite actors). On Tuesday October 12 I saw 'Casablanca' with Bogart and Ingrid Bergman and since then, almost 46 years ago, Sam has been playing it again!

In early November I saw 'Pittsburgh' and 'I Cover Chinatown.' There was also 'The Omaha Trail,' 'The Human Comedy,' and 'Flying Deuces.' On Christmas Day 1943 I went to 'George Washington Slept Here.' Jack Benny was the star.

That rings down the curtain on the 1943 movies in my diary. That was the forties, the era of Hollywood magic and the dancing nights; the time when you could have left your door open all night and no one would have bothered you; the era of Brylcreem and Brilliantine, Woodbine and Players and Gallaher Blues; the time when we all danced together in harmony and for us lads around Armagh and district, Belfast, the Big Smoke, was a long way away. It was the era of the half nights and the long nights in country halls. Most of all it was the decade when we got to know American life and more about the States than anywhere else in the world through the magic of the silver screen. There was nothing like a good movie, or even, come to that, just a movie. The war seemed a long way off, apart from the cinema newsreels and the ration books and the scarcity of fags.

Looking back now, I realise the last time I was at the pictures was to see 'Watership Down' in Belfast's Ritz. They don't make movies like they once did, but I am still spellbound when some of the old classics are shown on television.

Joe the clarinet player

Every night for a week, Joe the bicycle mechanic came riding into town on his bike and although it was May of the year, he still wore a heavy, well-worn black overcoat, cap – and in complete contrast, a whiter-than-white shirt and a big black dickey bow. On the carrier of the bike he had a long, slender black case strapped on, inside of which was his clarinet.

Joe, for many a long year, had been something of a loner; he had the reputation of being one of the best bicycle mechanics in the country and could have taken a buckle out of a wheel while he smoked a Woodbine. He parked his machine up an entry and then furtively made his way into the grand City Hall with his clarinet and case, trying to make sure nobody spotted him.

Taking place that whole week was the staging of the light opera 'Mauritana,' by the local Musical Society. I was one of the second violins and Joe was the clarinettist of the orchestra conducted by the late Sean O'Boyle who had studied in his time under the famous German, Carl Hardeback, in Belfast.

For weeks before the first night they'd been blue in the face trying to get Joe the mechanic to play, for they knew that he was one of the finest exponents of the clarinet in the north of Ireland in his heyday. Years before, Joe had vowed never to take the stage again, after playing in orchestras and dance bands right through the thirties. He told me once, that after years of playing at concerts and such, he became totally disillusioned with the whole thing, so he locked his clarinet away for good.

But Gerry the cobbler, another fine clarinet man who knew and played with Joe of old, finally broke Joe down and got him to play for a week in 'Mauritana.' And so here was Joe, with the old dickey bow on again making a reluctant comeback.

It was during rehearsals that I first had the pleasure of hearing Joe play. We had six rehearsals, but Joe only came to the first one and said he'd be back on opening night. Once through the score was enough for him.

During that week, each night at eight, Joe and his clarinet sang sweetly, high above the rest of the orchestra, despite a bit of screeching from one of the first violins. Each day he worked at the bikes and each night, Joe was back in the orchestra pit, a magnificent musician and the star of the show.

On the last night, following another virtuoso performance, Joe packed his clarinet into the case and crept out of the City Hall without saying he was away. He never came out to play again. What a waste of a great talent. The following Monday morning I called into the bicycle shop where he worked and there he was putting spokes in a wheel with the oil soiled cap on and the Woodbine fag in the mouth.

'Did you enjoy the show last week, Joe?' I asked. He barely looked up. 'Ach, it was all right' was his answer.

The music of Joe's clarinet was talked about for a long time after 'Mauritana.'

And the band played on

One evening towards the tail end of summer I was travelling along roads of yesterday in County Armagh. Rounding a corner I stopped, for there it was, looking as it did forty years ago, although grass was growing wild around it, even trying desperately to gain entrance by a window.

The little dance hall made of wood and zinc was now a hayshed, sitting in off the narrow winding road, but many a night I had danced away the hours there to the music of Jimmy McNamara on the accordion and Jimmy Murphy on the drums. As I gazed at it, I half expected the door to open and out would come my old dancing friends, mopping the sweat from their brow with large white hankies, smoking Wild Woodbines or Gallaher Blues. The mind can surely play tricks.

There used to be 'long nights' and 'half nights' here in this little hall close to the River Callan and I never missed a night there right through the forties. A half night ended at midnight and the long night went on till three or after in the morning. The long night attracted dancers who had already been to a half night somewhere else, maybe at Ballycrummy outside Armagh, an identical type of hall. They were gluttons for punishment and many was the early morning I went home on the bicycle with my shirt wringing wet with sweat and my mother swearing that as sure as anything I would take pneumonia or worse, for to her mind there was nothing worse than 'sweating and cooling.'

Admission charge to a half night was 1s 6d and the long night set you back half a dollar, payable at the door or later when your man went round with the hat. Even on a cold, winter night, it was like a Turkish bath inside that wee hall. And there were those who never missed a half night or a long night, yet never put a foot under them. Seating accommodation was sparse; long wooden forms joined together round the hall. Soon the place would be packed; some sat on another's knee, some hunkered down on the floor, some even lay on the floor. And all the while the band played on . . .

Minerals could be procured beside the small stage and it didn't take long to work up a druth if you were in a set of Lancers, D'Alberts, Sixteen Hand Reel or a Military Two-Step. A set of Lancers might last for 10 minutes and you bobbing up and down and doing your steps and swinging your partner and marching round and round until your head was as light as a cork.

Harry the master of ceremonies did not stand on ceremony and you could have heard him shouting out the figures of the dances away out on the Moy Road. Harry was a tireless wonder, for after a long night he was up before six again to go to his work as a ploughman on Castledillon Farm. He was known far and wide for his prowess as an M.C. and carried out these duties at different halls, even the plush City Hall in Armagh when there'd be an Irish-and-Old-Time dance on. Harry would see to it that everyone enjoyed themselves and wouldn't tolerate anyone sitting a dance out. 'Ye could have stayed at home if ye'd wanted to sit all night,' he'd shout at you. He didn't like to have wallflowers at his dances and often went as far as to lose the bap over them, dragging them onto the floor and whirling them round himself.

Cars were a rare sight at such dances in the forties and outside the halls, the roadside was cluttered with bicycles and your bike could have been left there for a week and it'd be still there when you went back. A lot of us young boyos never had a light on our bikes, either, and going home in pitch darkness, made it by radar for we knew every turn and twist of the way. One morning my friend Joe was travelling thus when suddenly he was cowped off the bike and landed on something which he was sure was the oul' Divil himself, but wasn't it a poor harmless little donkey lying contentedly in the centre of the road. Your man though he was sent for.

Going to these dances in the harvest time was pleasant. There was something in the air; the mist was over the meadow; stooks of corn dotted fields like silent sentinels; God was in His Heaven and all was right with our world, even though a terrible war was raging in foreign fields.

Big Jimmy McNamara, the accordion player, came on his bicycle all the way from Benburb with his 'box' strapped over his shoulders, but by the closing of the decade he had an Austin 12 car.

I used to go to this little dance hall with Red Jack, who was a terrible man for dancing. He could sing a song and was also an excellent bagpipe player. Jack worked with a farmer and his living quarters for many years were above the stable, illuminated by candle power and full of cowboy story books. And at the half night and long night there were the pretty girls all in a row and many a romance blossomed during an old-time waltz.

As I stopped by this little hall at the end of the summer I could still hear the music of the accordion and the voices inside. I drove on slowly and almost ran into a cow that had broken out of a field.

Maguire took the floor . . .

Most of the older generation have heard of the famous song about teaching McFadden to waltz. According to the song McFadden had two left feet, both a bit on the outsize, with the result that, although he had the dancing 'in his head' he couldn't get it transferred to his feet.

There were a right school of McFaddens in the country during the forties when dancing was a part of life in rural districts. One such fellow stands out in my memory, a tall, lanky chap by the name of Maguire. He was the divil for going to the dances and him all spruced up, but he couldn't put a foot under him; in fact he was a worse case than McFadden himself. Maguire would turn up at the country halls or in the town hall dressed to kill with his hair so shiny with fourpenny bottles of Brilliantine that the flies could have held a skating competition on it. He travelled on his bicycle, placing a large white hankie over the saddle to keep his trousers spotlessly clean.

I recall the night three or four of us (and Maguire) went to this dance in a wee hall not a hundred miles from the famous village of the Moy in County Tyrone. He just sat there on the bench and smiled at one and all, getting through about forty Gallaher Blues in the course of the night.

Before entering the hall he had said: 'I wonder will it be any good tonight?' What he meant by that was something of a mystery to the rest of us high steppers, for when a fellow sits all night blinded by his cigarette smoke watching others shaking a leg, how can a dance be said to be good or otherwise?

Time passed and almost a year later Maguire was still going to the dances but was by now something of a wallflower to one and all. Not that this seemed to worry him unduly for he always said that he would take the

107

floor for sure at the next hop, but roll on the next night
and Maguire was still sitting it out and puffing away.

Then on one memorable occasion at a dance up the
country, Harry the M.C. could stick Maguire no longer
and from the wee stage beside the three musicians he
made the dramatic announcement: 'Ladies and
gentlemen, we have a special trate for yez all the night.
Our friend Maguire here is going to take the flure for the
first time ever – in the very next dance, which will be a
foxtrot. So I would appeal to all to give him plenty of
elbow room and leg room.'

Maguire turned all colours and half-choked on a Gallaher Blue. Says he to Harry the M.C. in a frightened
voice: 'I'll get up the next night for sure, Harry.'

'That,' says Harry, 'is as I roved out Mr Maguire.
You're getting up now and that's all there's to it.'

So the band struck up 'Chattanooga Choo-Choo,' but
Maguire didn't budge and nobody else made a move.
Then Harry went down, hauled him onto the floor and
dragged him over to where Big Maggie, a strapping
dacent girl, was standing. If you were Fred Astaire you'd
have a hard job trying to steer Big Maggie round the
floor, for she was a sort of a Mrs McFadden, although fair
play to her, she never sat a dance out and even asked
fellows to dance. She was built all in one piece as they say
in the country. And there in the centre of the floor stood
Maguire and Big Maggie. 'Just let yerself go, Maguire, ye
boy ye,' said Harry and gave Maguire and Maggie a good
push and away they went to the Chattanooga Choo-
Choo. A grand round of applause accompanied by
cheers went up but Maguire hadn't progressed far when
down he went with Big Maggie on top of him. He looked
as if he needed the kiss of life but of course, this was
unheard of in those days. Harry hauled them both to
their feet and the band played on, with Maguire walking
all over Big Maggie's feet, and her smiling away radi-
antly, grand girl that she was.

Before the end of the 'round' however, Big Maggie was looking a bit peeved at all the clapping and cheering and Maguire walking over her feet and she looked as if she might give Maguire a belt on the lug. The band kept on playing and the pair of them were puffing as hard as that old Chattanooga train itself. Eventually, out of exhaustion the band stopped. Maguire staggered back to his corner and Big Maggie limped to her seat. Harry the M.C. announced from the stage: 'Ladies and gentlemen, Mr Maguire says he will never again sit another dance out and from now until we go home he'll step it out with any of you girls who fancy a burl.'

So like it or lump it, for the next two hours Maguire was up among the other dancers in everything from the Tango, Valeta Waltz and Hokey-Cokey. Harry wouldn't hear tell of him taking a breather. At night's end, Maguire was in a state of advanced fatigue, not to mention being dog tired. But surprise, surprise, at the end of the last dance, didn't he stand up in the middle of the floor and with that big, friendly smile said: 'Ladies and gentlemen, I have tonight made, as they say in France, my dancing debut and I hereby promise that you will never see me sitting one out again as long as my legs stick the pace.' With that, he turned, gave his brow a wipe with the hankie and went out, got on the bike and headed home, whistling 'La Paloma.'

And as time went on, Maguire kept his promise and danced the nights away. A year later he was one of the best dancers in the country with all the girls eager to take the floor with him.

'A little push was all Maguire needed,' said Harry the M.C.

Going dancing in the Morris 8 tourer

Big Tim, Barney, Pat and myself always felt like real swanks when we went dancing in John's Morris 8 tourer in the mid-forties. The little car, a 1938 model which John, a shopboy, kept tuned to perfection, purred along summer and winter roads like a Rolls Royce; the height of luxury as we were more often used to travelling by bicycle.

However, accommodating five tall men in the tourer was something of a squeeze, to say nothing of taking an agonising cramp in the leg and us dressed in our good suits. Big Tim said he'd be more at ease if he could have put his legs out through the window, but John, being a law-abiding citizen, wouldn't hear tell of that, saying we'd be the talk of the country if anyone saw us, never mind the risk of running up against an arm of the law.

On cold winter nights the journeys around County Armagh and beyond into Tyrone, were somewhat similar to an expedition to the Arctic and we knew how Captain Scott and such men must have felt. In the Morris 8 tourer there were two little plastic-like windows that flapped at the whim of the wind and through which a constant stream of freezing air flowed.

But such minor discomforts did not deter us, for like most young fellows of that time we were dancing mad, not that we were any great shakes on the dance floor, mind you. On such cold and frosty nights we wrapped heavy mufflers round our heads and at times Big Tim took one of the blankets off his bed with him.

On one exceptionally cold night we were zooming along at 35 miles per hour outside the town of Dungannon on our way to a dance in Omagh when John chanced to wander off the straight and narrow. He stopped the tourer to ask a chap walking up a hill with his bicycle how to get back onto the right road again. Well, your man took a look at the five of us all wrapped up, turned, jumped on the bike and was away *down* the hill like a blaze of whins. We must have looked like the Jesse James gang on wheels.

John was a great man for singing, being a member of the Cathedral choir in Armagh when Cardinal MacRory lived in Ara Coeli. He had a deep Paul Robeson-like voice and he usually gave a rendering of 'My Curly Headed Baby.' Big Tim preferred Frank Sinatra or Nelson Eddy. But just the same, when John had finished 'My Curly Headed Baby' we all said it was great and that he had the quare good voice and should be on the wireless. We were afraid that if we didn't praise him, John might take the hump and it would be back to the bikes.

Barney could only sing the first couple of lines of 'The Irish Rover' . . . 'In the year of Our Lord 1806 we set sail from the fair cove of Cork . . . We were sailing away with a cargo of bricks for the grand City Hall in New York . . .'

The only time he had sung it in what you might call 'public' was at a wedding party at Tullysaran and it took half the night to start him. The assembly that night were unanimous that it must go on record as the shortest song in the world. Pat could whistle like a curlew over a winter bog.

But this is by the way. On arrival at a dance hall, whether in town, village or country parish hall, John would first insist in having a peep inside before going in. At most halls that was possible by simply going round to the side and having a dekko through a window. But at one hall along the shores of Lough Neagh he had to climb on top of a large wooden barrel to see through the window and didn't the oul' barrel wobble, go into a spin and John fell into the muck and all the dogs about the place went mad barking, and a big black Labrador nearly pulled the trousers off him. So it was Home James right

off the reel with John looking as if he'd been pulled
through a ditch. He didn't sing 'My Curly Headed Baby'
that night and the four of us were in a sullen mood, never
speaking until we got back into Armagh.

Although we frequented many dance halls, Big Tim
never put a foot under him. He just stood there, never
sat, with the cigarette smoke blinding him. He said he
didn't dance because he never spotted a girl good looking enough. No, correction! I remember seeing Big Tim
dancing, if you could call it that, about twice in five years
– both Ladies' Choice.

Coming home one night (about three in the morning),
we were so hungry and the tourer was parked outside an
orchard at Loughgall so in we trooped, climbed the trees
and feasted on lovely Beauty of Bath apples.

And thus it continued until we came to the end of our
dancing days and the Morris 8 tourer went off the road.
Looking back now those dancing years of the forties
were happy and carefree. The cinema and the dance hall
and a packet of cigarettes – the age of innocent pleasures.
Big Tim and John have been married now for over 30
years and Pat tied the knot about 17 years ago. Barney's
still a bachelor and spends his time gardening, watching
old movies on TV and is addicted to the pipe and Walnut
Plug tobacco. I oftimes wonder if John ever sings 'My
Curly Headed Baby' to his family round the winter fire.

The wedding party in a byre with Red Jack

I had just landed home from the last house of the pictures one autumn night when Red Jack, who worked for a farmer across the fields, came tearing breathlessly into the house. 'C'mon quick!' say he, not taking time to sit down. 'Get yer oul' fiddle there and c'mon down to the Flush. Phil Doonican got married this mornin' and there's a bit of a weddin' party at his house.' The wedding house, he added was packed with people and there wasn't a craythur to play a note of music, and a wedding party was no wedding party without music and perhaps a dance.

I was no more than seventeen at the time and my mother bid Red Jack to take a chair and have a drop of tea, but he waved this aside, saying there wasn't time for that, as we'd have to go right away. I had just been after coming from 'Drums along the Mohawk' starring Henry Fonda in the Cosy Corner Picture House and images of that stirring Western movie were still flitting before the mind's eye and the wedding party at the Flush seemed a million miles away from the Mohawk Valley and Henry Fonda with his bearskin hat and blunderbuss. However, soon Red Jack and myself were zooming along the road with the fiddle case strapped to the carrier of my bicycle which had no light, but I knew the trail well and didn't really need illumination, and we'd hardly bump into a policeman at that time of night, seeing it was around midnight.

After almost running over an oul' lad standing at a corner in the dark we arrived at the wedding house – a whitewashed farmhouse with two big trees in the haggard. We parked the bikes and went in, me lugging the fiddle case under my oxter. Red Jack excitedly announced that the one-man band had arrived and the

113

cheers went up all round and I doubt whether Yehudi
Menuhin ever got as good a reception. Phil the groom
was dressed out in his wedding suit and white shirt with
hard collar and the carnation was still in the buttonhole
but by now it had withered somewhat. His bride Molly, a
decent girl whom I knew, was sitting full of smiles with
about a dozen other women. She came over and shook
hands, but when you're seventeen and after coming
from a great picture like 'Drums Along the Mohawk'
your wedding etiquette mightn't be all it should be. I
don't believe I even wished the pair the best of luck,
although I don't think by that stage they expected any
such greeting from me. Phil the groom was a tall, red-
faced fellow and as he drank a bottle of stout he didn't
seem all that much at ease in his new pin-stripe
wedding suit, but he said it was good of me to bring the
fiddle down at such short notice.

Phil and Molly had been going steady for about seven
or eight years, they said, and there were some folk in the
district who were adamant that they'd never get around
to tying the knot, but there you are; life is full of surprises
and judging by the happy expressions on Phil and
Molly's faces, it all seemed like the fulfilment of a lovely
dream. They'd been married that morning in Armagh
and went off to Dundalk for the day. A short honey-
moon, but at that time, Majorca and Corfu and such
exotic places were only names on the world's map. There
were couples who went for a few days to Dublin or, if
they had more money than sense, a week away down in
Killarney or even, Heaven's above, a week in London
itself. But Phil had said the good weather mightn't last
and he had a loc' of acres of corn to get down and
anyhow he wasn't the type to wander off afar and ramble
about doing nothing.

First, I was sat down to a good feed of lovely sand-
wiches, cakes, buns, tea and all that and I was glad to get
some sustenance, for 'Drums Along the Mohawk' was a

long picture and I had to queue up more than half-an-hour to get in so I had a right good appetite. While I was eating, the other men were lowering the cases of stout mixed with glasses of Bushmills and as a result all present were in a state of euphoria, for the ladies were partaking of wine and sherry and perhaps an odd wee Bush on the quiet.

Eventually I got the fiddle tuned to satisfaction and perched myself on top of a stool in the corner and away I went with foxtrots, quick-steps, two-steps, lancers, quadrilles and jigs and reels, and everyone took the floor, some of whom had never put a foot under them before. But this wasn't a 'Come Dancing' affair and nobody was all that fussy about what steps were taken. And sure with all the laughing and ya-hooing and the banter and crack, I might as well not have been there at all as the fiddle was scarcely audible above the merrymaking din. As the time wore on I was sweating profusely because there was still a bright fire burning in the stove and in addition, a more sobering aspect was the fact that I was now running out of tunes, not that anyone might have noticed. It was a great relief when Red Jack was called upon for a song and rendered a grand old ballad called 'The County Tyrone,' the first few lines of which went something like this:

My parents they told me
They ne'er could control me
A draper they'd make me
If I stayed at home.
But to make them all liars
I'll never deny her
I'm going to get married
In the County Tyrone . . .

Red Jack had a right good strong voice with a lilt to it and during the course of the song he kept his eyes closed. Halfway through the saga of love in Tyrone my mind wandered back to 'Drums Along the Mohawk' and marvelled at the bravery of Henry Fonda when he went along for a peace pow-wow with the big Indian Chief who looked more scary than Boris Karloff in 'Franken- stein.' I was jerked back to reality when the cheers and the clapping resounded at the end of Red Jack's song and I hoped he would be coaxed into singing an even longer one so that I would get a rest and try to dream up a handful more tunes, which was like asking for a miracle. By now the house was filled with cigarette and pipe smoke, added to by my own furtive draw on the odd Woodbine. At that time in the early forties people smoked their heads off and enjoyed it and there was never a mention of the risk of cancer or heart trouble. Didn't Henry Fonda roll his own smokes in 'Drums along the Mohawk?'

It must have been around three o'clock in the morning when young Tommy ran in and yelled right in the middle of 'The Queen Mary Waltz' 'The cow's calved!' And out everyone trooped, the men with bottle or glass in hand, to the byre to see the new arrival – a bonny brown healthy calf, lying there in the straw.

Of course, Phil the groom was delighted and immedi- ately proposed a toast to the new arrival. Furthermore, he proposed that we all stay in the byre and continue with the dance, song and general jollification. There was a lot more elbow room in the byre than the kitchen and a pleasant cool air came in through the open door and outside there was a bright harvest moon and a blue, starry sky.

A few more singers dutifully obliged with such as 'Dobbin's Flow'ry Vale,' 'The Old Rustic Bridge' and 'The Boys from the County Armagh.' I was then reques- ted to render a few fiddle solos so I scraped at 'The Frost is all over,' 'The Maid behind the Bar' and 'Danny Boy' to which one and all joined in. After that John Joe who had come out of Armagh sang a local ballad by the name of

'McKee's backyard' which went to the air of 'Phil the Fluter's Ball.'

What time did the wedding party end? I remember it was getting very bright over the horizon across the Callan River and the roosters had been crowing for an hour or more. No doubt some of the lads would go home for an hour or so and then come back for more and I later heard that the party continued all the following day and well into the night. But Red Jack and I had high-tailed it home on the bikes. It must have been a month later before I opened the fiddle case again.

The day Black Tam lost his whistle

He was called nothing but Black Tam because he had jet black hair, black eyebrows and being a roadman of the old school in the thirties, the tar was ground into his hands, not to mention his face, which most of the time looked as if it had never seen soap and water. Tam was a man of around forty when I knew him and he lived his lone a couple of miles outside Armagh. I suppose his proper Christian name was Tom, but in our part of the country every Tom was pronounced Tam.

I used to listen to him talking to men along the road of a summer night and I remember him saying that his great-grandfather had been a real cowboy out in the Wild West of America and that he had shot more men than there were buttons on your waistcoat breast. You see according to Black Tam his great-granda was at one time a sheriff in Dodge City, of all places, where there were all sorts of baddies on the prowl. There were men along the road who said Tam was the biggest liar in the whole county of Armagh and that included round by the gap of Mountnorris and home by Blackwater again, as the song goes.

One sunny Sunday Black Tam decided to head off for that popular seaside resort, a favourite of the boys from the County Armagh – Warrenpoint, or the 'Point as it was and still is more commonly called. There was an excursion by train and the return fare was half-a-crown. There were some who said the 'Point didn't hold a candle to the Rocks, which translated means Blackrock outside Dundalk. But Tam said he got the quare sickener the one and only day he went to the Rocks. It bucketed rain all day and the eating house where he got his tea was not just up to his expectations, for he maintained the 'tay' was innocent water scalded to death, so after that he had

118

stuck to the 'Point with the odd trip across to Omeath in the boat.

However Black Tam's latest excursion to the 'Point did not prove a very happy one. He was crossing over in the boat to Omeath with a handful of others, among them a chap playing 'The Mountains of Mourne' on an oul' accordion, an appropriate tune for the place, although I'd say that if the man who wrote the song, the bold Percy French himself, had heard this rendition he'd have been none too pleased, as the accordion ran out of wind half time and had hardly a puff left in its bellows. And just when the boat was about halfway across didn't this somewhat inebriated passenger get up and stagger over to Black Tam, threatening to throw him overboard as if he were Captain Bligh of the Bounty. Why would anyone wish to throw Black Tam overboard? Well, there were, they tell me, a brave lot who would love to have had the chance of heaving him overboard in the deepest part of Carlingford Lough. Don't ask me why.

This boyo said he wanted to throw him overboard because he reminded him of somebody he did not particularly like. Now Black Tam, whose great-granda had been a gun-toting sheriff of Dodge City, didn't care for people messing about with him and he grabbed your man saying if he didn't sit down he'd knock him into the middle of next week and with that gave him a push and the inebriated fellow fell back into his seat. In the process Black Tam slipped and fell against the side of the boat and soon to his dismay discovered he'd cracked the plate of his false teeth.

Since that incident on the way to Omeath, Black Tam lost his whistle and for a countryman to lose his whistle is indeed a harrowing tragedy, especially Tam for he was one of the best whistlers in the townland. Once you get a crack in your false teeth plate, away goes your whistle and you can try to whistle till the cows come home and yet not be able to whistle a recognisable bar of 'The Oul

Bog Road.' So this is the reason he had no fond memories of his last trip to the 'Point.

Perhaps the moral of what happened to Tam is that it is a bad thing at times to resemble someone else, especially when you're away from home and particularly in a wee boat.

Black Tam was fond of putting a few bob on the horses in Armagh and gained quite a reputation of being able to pick the odd good winner. Old Ned who lived along the road was always trying to get a winner and so he was regularly on the look-out for Tam to find out what he fancied and get him to take his bet with him. As time passed, Black Tam got a real sickener of Old Ned and his sixpence each way bets and tried his best to avoid him.

He kept telling Old Ned that backing the nags was a mug's game and that the bookie always won, and if he kept on with his tanner and bob bets on a regular basis he'd end up with no arse in his trousers, for when the gambling bug got a grip you just couldn't stop. But it was no use. Ned said he'd see to it that he'd keep the arse in his trousers. One day Old Ned hailed me on the road to ask if I'd seen Black Tam. 'You never can see that boyo when ye want him. I want to try and get a winner to buy myself a new cap.'

Black Tam started to take another road into town and the bookies, but although it added a few extra miles, he said it was better than encountering Ned and his tanner each-way bets. Well, by the appearance of Black Tam you'd never think he was a dab hand at picking winners for he wore an oul' coat and cap as black as his hands, but then again, appearances can be deceiving and perhaps he was stashing all his winnings under the mattress, a well known 'bank' in parts of the country.

But betting apart, Black Tam never regained his whistle for the simple reason that following the day he cracked the plate of his false teeth, the crack got worse and worse until he eventually had to take the teeth out and leave them in the cupboard and go gummy. And he had no intention of getting a new set of false teeth seeing how much they'd cost and he never pictured himself as Robert Taylor anyhow, and if people didn't like the way he looked with no top teeth, then they could just lump it. But ever after there was one thing he regretted and that was not being able to whistle 'The Oul' Bog Road.'

PULLING APPLES BY THE BOX

Clodding spuds in the potato field

Gathering spuds in the potato fields of county Armagh and throughout Ulster is now but a memory. Time was in the thirties and forties when a boon of men would descend on the field at eight o'clock in the morning and get down to the back-breaking job of filling the baskets behind a pair of horses, or worse still, the tractor. At the end of the week, on Saturday night that is, you got ten or fifteen bob in your hand for your week's toil and then it was home to get a wash-up and head up the town to the Cosy Corner Picture House or the City Cinema for the last house at nine o'clock, to sit back with ten Woodbine cigarettes and a bar of Mountain Maid toffee to enjoy a good cowboy movie with Johnny Mack Brown or the young John Wayne as one of the Three Mesquiteers or a Jimmy Cagney gangster story where poor Jimmy ('I was framed') always ended up behind bars in San Quentin.

On the way home at eleven o'clock you'd call into Latchie Cafolla's Chip Shop in English Street for a fish supper which cost eightpence with all the salt and vinegar you required. But back to the spud field. Gathering spuds was a tough job but there was light relief in the 'divarsion' of clodding spuds while you worked. If you've never gathered spuds during this era, which ran from October to November, then it is very unlikely that you will know very much about this type of sport. As you proceeded with the task of gathering the spuds spewed out by the digger into the wire basket, you might well have found yourself the target for the odd flying potato thrown at you from another gatherer across the field. If the farmer himself didn't chance to be around, the exchange of shots could well have become quite regular and mind you, it was no joke getting a crack with a spud right on the kisser or the back of the neck, or other parts of the anatomy when least expected.

But the whole secret was to keep a cool head and not retaliate, for if you lost the bap you were liable to get 'lamskuttered' with more than enough flying spuds. There's a word you'll not find in the Oxford Dictionary. They say that a lot of our Ulster words were used by Shakespeare himself, but I'm wondering if the Bard ever used the word 'lamskuttered?'

Clodding spuds at the harvesting was looked upon as good, clean and healthy fun which broke the monotony, for bending over and looking into the good earth at close quarters all day can certainly become monotonous as any spud gatherer would have told you in all honesty.

If any member of the spud gathering team had a reputation of being what was known in the country as a 'crab' he would have found himself the target for a barrage of flying spuds when least expected. There were various ways of throwing the spud and the hinchers were deadly for they could deliver the spud at the rate of no-man's-business. But at dinnertime when the spud gatherers assembled in the house for their dinner of spuds, cabbage and bacon, there was never any animosity and the clodding was never brought up in conversation, for the simple reason that the lads were too hungry to think of such trivialities. At the farmer's dinner table where we gathered down the Loughgall Road, one of the workers, a decent fellow, was something of a Walter Mitty and during dinnertime would recount his adventures while driving a big army truck down the Burma Road. Everyone listened intently while they lathered into the spuds, cabbage and bacon, knowing full well that your man Willie John had never been any further than Portadown on a Saturday night for the dance in the Savoy where Jimmy Millsop sang 'Ghost Riders In The Sky.'

Willie John had worked for this farmer since he'd left

school and Jim the farmer, an easy-going man, knew full well that your man had never been within a hound's growl of the Burma Road, but he nodded in agreement and apparent amazement at everything that was said. Willie John had a wild imagination, but Jim or anyone else never did pull him up on his stories. And that was long before Danny Kaye played the part of Walter Mitty in Hollywood. But there we were, sitting round the table and there was Willie John telling his tales of dicing with death on the Burma Road and many other roads into the bargain. But Willie John was a great grafter on the farm, a tireless chap who would tackle any job from tying corn to pitching flax out of a flax-hole. On Saturday night he rewarded himself with a couple of pints in The Garden of Eden pub and a fish-and-chip supper out of Latchie Cafolla's.

Apart altogether from gathering and clodding the spuds of a late October evening, the job of assembling the spuds in pits or 'bings' as we called them in Armagh, was something of an art in itself and left to a couple of the experts like Willie John. When the spuds would be assembled into a pile of about three feet high, they'd then be covered carefully with clay, then a layer of straw and on top of that another covering of clay. This would ensure that the 'bing' would be safe against winter frosts.

In most parts of the country now, the potato crop is taken into the barn when gathered, but I'm told that the odd farmer still clings to the the old method of putting them in 'bings' and they'll tell you that a well made 'bing' will preserve the spuds better than any barn.

Does anyone 'scraw' potatoes these times? 'Scrawing' spuds is no picnic. The farmer who 'scraws' the spuds doesn't use a digger, but runs a plough right down the middle of each drill and the gatherer has to come behind and dig deep with his hands to unearth each potato, many of which are sliced by the plough. I remember giving a neighbour a day or two at 'scrawin'' the spuds around Halloween and going home at night thinking I had no hands left on me at all, for the fingers were completely numb with the cold at digging into the deep earth to find the elusive potato. But all was forgotten when we sat down to a grand tea in the house with good, warm soda griddle bread, loads of butter and jam and a couple of lovely boiled eggs. It was usually the very small farmer who 'scrawed' his spuds, mostly for his own consumption, but there was a great satisfaction when the work was done and as the poet said, 'the plowman homewards plods his weary way.'

Anyhow, a day at the potato gathering, especially of a pleasant October day was a refreshing experience and to relieve the monotony of the back-breaking task there was always the clodding to lift your spirits. And at that time in the early forties, a farmer would have looked at you if you'd mentioned getting spuds from Cyprus!

Pulling apples by the box

The Loughgall area of Armagh has long been famous for its orchard lands and its great Bramley apple, second to none in the British Isles or anywhere else for that matter. In Maytime the hundreds of orchards are like one big garden with their tantalising blossom of white and sea-shell pink, each little blossom an individual flower. Years ago the late Cardinal Logue of Armagh returned from a trip which included Japan. From the pulpit of the Cathedral on the hill, he said that the cherry blossom of Japan was marvellous, but it couldn't hold a candle to the apple blossom around Armagh in the spring-time.

These times, apple-pullers (we never call it 'picking') can earn up to about £120 a week harvesting the apples from September right through to October. And this recalls the days we used to pull the apples for sixpence (2½p) per box and every box held 50 lbs. This was later raised to ninepence a box, the price of admission to the stalls of the Cosy Corner Picture House. We 'pulled by the box' and it was up to yourself to make a right day's pay, but there were some very good pullers who came down from the Mill Row and could knock up a hundred boxes a day – not great money now but in the early forties, money was worth money. One fellow called Tommy from the Mill Row pulled around a hundred boxes every day and was ready to go home at four o'clock as fresh as a daisy. He was reckoned the best apple-puller about the country and was always in demand at that time of year.

There's a knack to pulling apples like most other jobs and some chaps just had not got it and at day's end had little to show for climbing up and down the ladders around the trees in the orchard. Of course a fairly young orchard was much handier to work in than an orchard with old, high and twisted trees and when the owner wasn't looking you'd be sorely tempted just to give the laden branches a good shaking and then gather the apples off the ground. But this was looked upon as a cardinal sin when pulling apples, for once an apple hit *terra firma* it had to be classed as a windfall, a shame especially if it was a good Bramley. If an apple is slightly damaged it will not 'keep' for long and there's the story of the one bad apple in the barrel. The good and careful apple puller will get his ladder into the correct position then ascend with bucket, on the handle of which is attached a homemade wire 'click' for hanging over the branches and he will set about pulling off apple by apple and placing them carefully in the bucket, and some pullers put a good handful of grass in the bucket to act as a cushion. When the bucket is full but not overflowing, the puller descends and empties his bucketful carefully into a wooden box.

It can be a very pleasant job pulling apples of a bright autumn morning when the grass is still wet with the dew. Up among the branches you feel cut off from the world and when you're 'pulling by the box' time seems to fly.

During the early days of the last war the Armagh apples were in great demand and the boon of pullers could be seen heading off down the Loughgall Road every morning singing and whistling. I remember once being called upon to pull an orchard on a Sunday, the demand being so urgent. Jack who owned the orchard bought some bottles of lemonade and a few cakes out of Bob's shop. But it was like throwing buns to a bear, dividing cakes and baps and bracks and such among half-a-dozen hungry pullers, for there's nothing gives you as good an appetite as perched up an apple tree and you filling your bucket to the air of Molly Riley.

Some orchards were isolated and we often ran out of Woodbines or Park Drive so we used to go out to the road and wait for someone coming along on the way to the town and get them to bring some fags down, but at times we'd be dying for a smoke and your man wouldn't come back for hours, perhaps going to the bookies or the pub and there was always the danger that such a messenger might well smoke the fags himself.

My friend Davy said he couldn't pull apples if he hadn't a smoke. He was almost six feet tall at sixteen or seventeen and was an excellent apple-puller, if the notion was on him that is, and when he was in form he could strip a tree while others would just be getting dug in. He was agile on the top, precarious branches, a bit of a Tarzan and would take a break at times and swing through the branches and from one tree to another, shouting out 'Me Tarzan, Me Tarzan!' Coming on in the afternoon, Davy oft-times lost heart and began shaking the odd branch so as to get his boxes filled. What oul' Johnny didn't know would do him no harm, said Davy, then setting to gathering up any leaves that were shake down with the apples, for leaves like this were a dead give-away to the fact that there had been a bit of shaking going on.

Pulling apples for William and Robbie was a heart-scald. Especially for William, who thought as much of one solitary apple as he did about a cow. So in order to protect any falling fruit he spread some jute bags round the bottom of the tree to soften the fall and save them from any damage. William was a dacent spud but he hated to part with a shilling. He didn't believe in paying a puller by the box but on Saturday night he'd hand you a pound or two. I recall once pulling there for a few days and come that Saturday night William says 'I'll give ye a loc' of shillins' when ye come back on Monday.' But I was looking forward to going to the last house of the Cosy Corner Picture House and a fish supper afterwards in Cafolla's, it being Saturday night. And into the bargain I hadn't a smoke left, only a butt of a Woodbine I was keeping for the walk back home down the hill.

William himmed and hammed but I didn't give in so at

last he went into the house and came back and reluctantly handed me a ten-bob note. 'There, you're takin my last shillin' with ye the night,' he said. But I wasn't feeling sentimental and grabbed the money, for ten bob was ten bob at that time and into the bargain William had the house full of money as anybody could tell you, but he just couldn't come to terms with parting with it.

One thing when you were pulling for William, he always gave you a good feed of tea, bread, butter and jam. There were others who would not even provide boiling water for you to brew up your own drop in the orchard and that's the truth and many a time you had to sit down and eat your bread and butter without a mouthful of tea or anything else.

At times during the day, the lads used to start clodding apples at one another and at dinnertime, someone would have a 'bullet' or road bowl with them and we'd go out onto the road and have a few shots.

And when the apples had been duly harvested throughout the scores of fine orchards, it was time to gather the potatoes, the best job in the world for giving you a good sore back which slowed you down until near Christmas! Gathering after horses was bad enough, but with a tractor at your heels it was ten times worse. Why, you never had time even to take a drag of a Woodbine, but you always slept well that night and there was Sloan's Linament in the wee bottle to soothe your tired limbs.

By November the orchards were stark and bare. Shakespeare got it right:
'That time of year thou mayest
In me behold
When yellow leaves or none
Or few, do hang
Upon those boughs
Which shake against the cold,
Bare ruin'd choirs
Where late the sweet birds sang.

On Lough Neagh's banks

As a schoolboy I spent the long summer break on the farm of my Uncle Barney at a place called Columcille in the townland of Derrylard on the shores of Lough Neagh, eight miles out of Portadown. My mother, born and bred at the lough had told us it was a common sight in her young days to see women carrying big baskets of fish on their head from Maghery away up to Armagh, a good seventeen miles. The fishermen, maybe a father, husband or brother would have been out fishing on the lough most of the night, casting their nets as far as Toome. When they came ashore just after dawn the womenfolk would be waiting with their strong, homemade wicker baskets. With few words spoken, the baskets would be filled with the famous Lough Neagh pollen and off the women would go with the baskets on their heads, along narrow, winding roads through Annaghmore and Loughgall, to the market in Armagh city.

Some wore sturdy boots laced to the ankle and others plodded along in clogs. They'd arrive in Armagh around mid-day, sell the fish and after something to eat, lost no time in setting off for home again.

I have many happy memories of the roads round Lough Neagh. In the evenings when the sun would dip out of sight behind the Tyrone hills on the other side of the lough and the curlew cried eerily over Coney Island, I'd sit on the big stone at the Bannfoot on the 'back road' to Lurgan and listen to men tell stories. I became very friendly with a tall man of the lough, called Frank, and would stay with him when he'd be painting or repairing his boat. The boat, he said, had belonged to his father before him. He was a footloose fellow and whenever he'd take the notion, he'd pack his bag and head for

Belfast and the boat for Scotland, and stay away months at a time working on the lighters on the Clyde. Then one day he'd come walking up Columcille Road and everyone knew the rover had returned.

Frank was always a welcome caller in any of the ceili houses from Maghery to the Bannfoot and beyond. He could sing a song and spin a yarn and keep a night's crack going. Maghery, a quiet little hamlet at the mouth of the Lower Bann was a favourite mecca for Scottish visitors, most of them related to the locals. A couple of nights a week during July and August there'd be 'big nights' in the local hall for the 'Scotchies' and it was here that Frank took the limelight, acting as Master of Ceremonies for the dancing and general jollification – and more so when there was a mouthful or two of drink on the job.

The master teller of tales along that part of the lough shore was old John who lived in a secluded spot. Many a night I sat there, drinking strong tea and listening to his stories of life round Lough Neagh and of the terrible night when a father and his two sons set out to fish and never came back. Was it a freak wave that toppled the boat? Or was their catch too heavy? It remained a mystery, and of course any loughsider will tell you that the lough has claimed at least one victim every year from time immemorial.

One sunny summer afternoon I made the boat trip with a couple of young friends from Maghery to Washing Bay on the Tyrone side. The fisherman used his oars until we skirted Coney Island, then setting a westerly course he hoisted sail and away we went, skimming gracefully over the placid waters. The skipper then lay down and had a nap, leaving us alone with the screeching gulls, but awoke again to land us safely at Washing Bay. Coming home, there was a sports meeting there that day, there wasn't a boat to be seen so we had to walk back round the huge lough, a good ten or twelve miles.

I always went to my Uncle Barney's towards the end of June when his large strawberry crop was being harvested. The average strawberry crop consisted of around five acres and this was the family mainstay. Self-sufficient, Barney like all others had a couple of milking cows, pigs and hens and ducks and a pony and cart. At this time the strawberries had to be picked daily and we were out in the fields from early morning till almost dusk when the dealers came to take the crop to the Belfast market. Up until twenty years ago, a 32 lb case of strawberries fetched the grower not much more than £2 and they were picked into 1 lb punnets. There was also a considerable crop of black currants and raspberries to be harvested and many a day I also worked at the haymaking, but I was never there for the gathering of the potatoes in the autumn.

Uncle Barney, in the strawberry or hayfield, lit his pipe from a burning turf carried out from the hearth. It 'mooted' all day and could be 'blown' into life when he felt like a smoke. The family, like all others had their own moss or turf bog and digging and footing turf hadn't charged from my mother was a girl and had to join in the work with the turf spade; cutting turf was a job calling for skill. During the thirties and forties turf was the only fuel used for the open hearth fire and the lovely aroma of the turf smoke wafting on the soft summer air was a delight.

For years the ferryman at the Bannfoot was a Mr Wilson who operated the wooden ferry over the Upper Bann by pulling a gigantic rope.

Nowadays you won't find a field of strawberries along the lough at Columcille. Instead you'll see lettuces galore growing under polythene tents called tunnel houses – 120 feet long and costing up to £500 a 'house.' The bleak boggy fields are now dotted with these tents and the growers will tell you it was a blessing to be rid of the strawberries, for the lettuce brings in money all the year round. The average tunnel house holds 300 dozen lettuces.

The lettuce revolution around Columcille and Maghery, began some years back when a couple of men tried them in the open ground – and seeing how well the seed took to the rich, peaty soil, the next logical step was sowing under polythene. From then on, the Lough Neagh lettuce mushroomed and when I was last there about eight or ten years ago, 20 growers planted one million lettuces and today most of the north of Ireland's lettuces have their roots at Lough Neagh. My cousin John who works the farm at Columcille takes the lettuce to the Belfast market, each load consisting of 400 dozen, packed in cartons. He has to be at the market when it opens at five o'clock in the morning, but an early traffic-free run down the M1 doesn't take long and he can be back home before seven.

My father was a Lough Neagh man and actually lived on Coney Island for a spell in his young days. He once told me that during a big freeze-up the people came from near and far to skate out to Coney from Maghery, a distance of a mile. During the thirties and forties, the area around Maghery, Columcille and the Bannfoot was a closely-knit rural community where neighbour dropped into neighbour's house and told stories, sang songs and played music around a hearty turf fire. It is still a closely-knit community, but now King Coal is used for fuel in the modern fireplace and a bag of turf is as rare as a punnet of strawberries and they're whizzing about in cars, doing their shopping in Portadown and Dungannon and the young ones think nothing of heading off to Belfast for a night's entertainment at cinema or theatre. But we can hope that the lough itself, the largest lake in the British Isles will remain unchanged for ever and the older folk will tell you that they could not live anywhere else.

Big Mick and the thresher

Whether Big Mick ever thought of the autumn as the season of mists and mellow fruitfulness is debatable. He sauntered through life with the belief that the man who made time made plenty of it and as a result never had to see the doctor about high blood pressure or such afflictions.

He lived in a wee white-washed cottage up the loanen off the main road. There was always the great odour of wood smoke emanating from his chimmey for he disdained the use of coal in the grate and had half the townland chopped down for firewood. Especially from the heels of autumn on through the winter, great plumes of pure white smoke rose up through the tall trees. Of all wood his favourite fuel was the ash for he maintained it burned better and longer and also kept the chimney clean.

Big Mick sawed up his wood in the haggard and piled the chopped or sawn blocks beside the grate to get a seasoning. A good fire, a mugful of strong tea and a pipe was all he asked from life but he had to be on the pad as he called it, most of the time, to achieve this. He had a few hens and ducks and now and again, not too often, put a duck in the pot for a good feed of duck broth.

At certain times of the year, when the rush was on down on the local farms, he was called upon to lend a hand at the spud dropping, (and gathering), and at harvest time tying grass-seed, barley and corn or behind the thresher. For his long day's toil he might receive ten bob and a bite of grub.

And this takes us to October when Big Mick was despatched to the top of the steam threshing mill to loose the sheafs of corn, a job which was never very popular around threshing time, unless you were a glutton for punishment. Big Mick at the outset made a quiet request to be put on the bags at the rear of the mill, but he was ordered to get aloft and have a bit of sense. Up there he wielded the big knife to loosen the sheaves tossed up to him in abundance from all points of the compass. He would be seeing golden stalks of corn in his sleep.

'The ten bob that I shall earn on the top of that mill shall rightly be termed blood money.' he muttered as he climbed up, complaining of the rheumatism in his leg as he did so. The men who were pitching up the sheaves knew the mood of Big Mick, and cruel beings that they were kept tossing the stuff up thirteen to the dozen. Very soon he was completely submerged in sheaves, waving the knife about in apparent wild abandon and shouting down: 'Catch yerselves on, ye bloody gets yez. If I go down I'll put one of yez into the mill!'

George, who was feeding the loosened sheaves into the mill (a job calling for great timing and expertise) was by now showing shocked concern and called for a halt to the entire proceedings. Suddenly there was this dull 'thumph, bumph' from the mill and the big wheel with the big belt attached to the steam thresher itself, ground to a halt, as if it hadn't the will to go on. There was consternation. The man who was feeding clambered down from the mill and one and all began walking around the mill to try and discover what had happened. Then from under the pile of sheaves on top of the mill slowly emerged the figure of Big Mick. Calmly he came down the narrow ladder, in his socks and sat down on an apple box and proceeded to light his pipe.

Black Jack, who was at the bags exclaimed: 'Look, Mick must have lost his waterboots up there.' Well, Big Mick was minus his waterboots, or Wellingtons as some folk called them. Big Mick calmly explained that the pressure was so great from the sheaves he was loosing that both his waterboots had slipped off his feet and had gone down the mill. And from the back of the thresher, Dick

came on the scene in a splutter. 'Look' says he, holding
aloft pieces of black rubber in both hands, 'this came out
of the mill and that's what put the spanner in the works.'

'Dammit if they're not what's left of Big Mick's waterboots.' exclaimed Black Jack. 'If they are,' said the
thresher man himself, 'they've been the instigation of
breaking my mill. Wads of oul 'rubber like that would
choke any mill'!

That put an end to the threshing for the day for by now
it was getting on in the afternoon. The thresher man said
he'd have to get a man to have a look at the mill and with
a bit of luck they just might get it going for the next day.

Big Mick proclaimed calmly that the owner of the mill
or oul' Fred the farmer would have to buy him a new pair
of waterboots for he would have to walk up the road
home in his socks and hadn't another boot or shoe in the
house to wear. As he started off walking he turned back
and said: 'I could have been killed up on top of that oul'
mill and it's only because God was looking over me that I
wasn't pulled into the mill with my waterboots, for I was
asked to do the work of four men up there. If I don't get
the price of a new pair of waterboots tomorow, I shall
have no alternative but to seek legal advice.' As calm as
you like, he was too.

Black Jack watched him hobble off in his socks 'Ye
know' he whispered to George, 'I think Big Mick was
getting it so tight on the mill he just took off his oul'
waterboots and dumped them in, knowing it would end
the threshing.'

As they said in that part of the country Big Mick didn't
come up the river in a bubble.

Dan was your man

Around our part of the country it was said that oul' Dan's house was not the best place to visit if you were fed up and far from home. There was something in that, too, for whenever you called in you were confronted by a few of the most miserable expressions you'd come across in a month of Sundays.

There was the clock wagging mournfully on the wall, the paraffin oil lamp with the blackened globe on the table and around the spark of a fire sat the Job's Comforters. If you were in right form on arrival the odds were that you'd leave in a state of deep depression. Dan himself was a wee ferret-faced character who looked as if a good dinner would kill him and if you were to believe him the whole world was set on nothing else but trying its best to do you a bad turn. Times with him were always getting worse, with no bright glimmer of hope on the horizon nor light at the end of the tunnel. Money, he said, always managed to elude him so he was forced to live on stirabout and buttermilk.

The couple of acres he owned would never yield a crop, he maintained; the corn grew downwards and the spuds were the size of marbles, 'marvels' as he called them. Up the country we called marbles, marvels. Dan said that most of his forefathers were wiped out during the dark days of the Famine when the sheep and cattle died and the blight came on the spuds and the poor folk died of starvation by the wayside. He also swore that Ireland was never the Land of Saints and Scholars. 'All a dammed myth' he said. 'Half of the people couldn't write their name and the other half never get down on their knees to mouth a prayer day or night, so where were your saints and scholars?'

But Dan your man knew how we came to get that

139

reputation. It all started with one of those Spanish soldiers of fortune who chanced to anchor his loot-laden galleon in Carrickfergus one day in May. He spots this oul' lad down on his knees in a field and right off the reel, took him for a saint. The Spaniard didn't know that the oul' fellow was scrawing spuds. Looking the other direction this Spanish boyo sees this other oul' lad sitting on a big stone, with his nose buried in a book, so he thought he must be a great Irish scholar, wise in the wisdom of the world, reading Socrates or Plato. But was he a scholar? 'Have a titter a wit,' says Dan 'He was just trying his best to cast a bad luck spell on your man who was scrawin' the spuds.'

So away goes the Spanish adventurer back to sunny Spain where they cannot grow Bramley apples or throw a game of road bowls and such. And when he gets home he tells one and all that the Irish must be all saints and scholars. Everywhere else he went over the Seven Seas he told them the same and soon the whole world looked upon Ireland as the Land of Saints and Scholars.

That was the sort of stuff you heard as you sat foundered round Dan's spark of a fire, with the result that his regular visitors were soon indoctrinated into his way of thinking and looking at life. If you had entered with even a 'good night' salutation they'd have given you a look that would have made a pagan bless himself. 'No two ways about it,' said Dan, 'when the Angel Gabriel at the end of the world blew his big hunting horn, everybody would get their just desserts and be hurled headlong into the bottomless pit.'

Dan said that if it were possible to return to earth after kicking the bucket, he wanted to come back as a pigeon so that if perchance there are any crops of corn left, he'd enjoy being able to have a feed right there in front of whoever owned it, because he wouldn't be an ordinary pigeon, but a sort of a ghost pigeon that couldn't be shot. One of the regulars called Reuben was Dan's No.1 dis-

ciple and he had a face like a Lurgan spade and a wet
Sunday in Mullabrack. Reuben said there wasn't a
dacent man or women left in all of Ireland and they'd all
get up in the middle of the night to do you a bad turn. He
too lived on stirabout and buttermilk and stewed the
same tay four times.

Oul' Dan's dead and gone this many a year and there
are some people in the district who'd tell you in all
sincerity that a big well-fed looking pigeon with an evil
eye forever cooing about the place is really Oul' Dan and
that the oul' crow perched in the tree watching every
move of everybody is Oul' Reuben.

Said Black Jack: 'When you come to think of it thon oul'
pigeon, if you happen to get a close dekko at it and its
oul' evil eye looking right through you, is the born spit of
Oul' Dan . . .'

The leaving of Ballyatteracap

According to the old song wasn't it the curse of emigration that has left parts of Ireland, north and south, with nothing but the curlew and snipe over the bog and meadow. You pass along roads and lanes where the old homes are but ghosts of the past, the families scattered to the four winds of the world.

And still they keep going from townlands like Ballyatteracap: the stout lads and fair lassies pack their bags and some of them never make it home again . . .

Picture if you will a country kitchen in Ballatteracap where the mother and son are bidding farewell as the son is off for London in the morning . . .

Mother: And so you're goin' away aff at last, are ye?

Son: Ah am. Ah'm goin' this time, Ma.

Mother: Lord, but you've talked long enough about it, so ye have.

Son: Aye, Ah have that in troth.

Mother: You're headstrong, mad to get away. But maybe when you're away a while ye'll be wishin' ye were back home again.

Son: Ah'm no wee lad, Ma. If Ah don't make a move now, I'll be too oul'.

Mother: O aye, go on and think about yourself. What about me? Maybe I'll be in the churchyard before ye even think of writin.' Some childer are a bad rarin'. Ye do your best for them, but they couldn't care a tuppenny dang for ye when it suits them.

Son: Ma, why d'ye go on like that? Dammit, I'm the last of the Mohicans. I've given the best years of my life to Ballyatteracap.

Mother: Ye'll niver larn sense.

Son: Ma, Ah'm thirty six and have been muck to the oxters since I was a lad. Muck to the oxters and niver a jingle in my pocket. Call that livin'?

Mother: Clean muck is not dirt.

Son: I've done my purgatory here in Ballyatteracap. Let the oul' fella tighten himself up a bit. He always thought he had me for a bit of a lig, doin' everything that had to be done from Monday to Sunday. I wanna see a bit of life before I'm not fit to enjoy it. We're all dead here if we only had the wit to stiffen.

Mother: Yer da is gettin' to be an oul' man.

Son: It'll do him good to have to roll up the sleeves for a change. Sure he never hardly does a hands-turn when he has an eejit like me to do it for him.

Mother: And that's the thanks yer father gets, eh? Aye, some childer are a bad rarin.' Ah suppose ye'll be on for pickin' some good for nothing hussy over in London and maybe gettin' married.

Son: Ah am not contemplatin' anything like that.

Mother: Ye'll sup sorrow, boy. Ye'll wish ye were back with yer oul' Ma, who gave you everything.

Son: Ma, no harm to ye, but you're inclined to exaggerate now and then. I've worked here for my keep and little more.

Mother: Ye niver had to boil a kettle to make a drop of tay, had ye? Everything was handed to ye. Aye, ye'll find the quare change in London, where they'd walk over ye and not care if ye were lyin' in the street starvin'.

Son: Ma, when I get to Camden Town and join
            up with Robbie and William from the Wee
            Brae and get workin' and make good
            money, I'll send ye home some every
            week. That'll put the smile on yer face,
            eh? But watch that the oul' lad doesn't get
            his hands on it or it'll go into the oul' tick
            on the bed, a prisoner from here to
            eternity. Scrooge was an amateur in
            miserly practice when it comes to the oul'
            fella.
Mother: A thrifty man, always thinkin' of a rainy
            day.
Son: Many a rainy day I seen and he wouldn't
            have gave me ten bob if it was to keep me
            out of jail, so he wouldn't. Rainy days,
            aye. But in London I'll have money in my
            pocket like all the others there. I'll not call
            the King me uncle. But I'll send you home
            some, Ma.
Mother: Live horse and you'll get grass. Ah
            wouldn't like to be puttin' on the kettle
            for the postman to bring it. Ye'll be stuck
            in the pubs like the rest of them that went
            away, throwin' yer money round you,
            just like your Uncle Tam who went to
            New York and drunk the piece out and
            niver could gather the fare to come home,
            and didn't he die there and lies buried
            there the day. Aye, some childer are a
            bad rarin'.
Son: You're a hard woman, Ma.
Mother: And you knowin' that there's not a
            mornin' I don't be overcome with the
            awful pains tearin' at my body. No
            thought for the ones that rared
            them.

Son: Ma, give over, will ye. You're healthier than I am and the doctor tould me that himself not a month ago.

Mother: D'ye mind the night ye sung 'The Oul' Mud Cabin on the Hill' when your Uncle Dan came up from Tandragee. Was it last winter or the winter afore? And then him and you and your da went away to the pub and rolled home full as the Boyne.

Son: Ah mind that. I do surely. And sure I never heard the end of it from you, did Ah?

Mother: Ye'll not have many to listen to ye singin' in London.

Son: Ah'm not goin' to London to sing to people.

Mother: Ye have some right quare notions, so ye have. Even when ye were a wee lad I always knew you had a bit of a wild strake in ye. It always comes out, sooner or later.

Son: Wild strake? I was only in Belfast twice in my life and that was the farthest I ever got, except for a couple of Sundays at Warrenpoint and over in the oul' boat to Omeath and twice in Bangor and once in Portrush. Wild strake aye. The Wild Colonial Boy, eh? Come in Dungannon, I know yer knock!

Mother: Ye've talked a right while about goin' away and now you're goin' off.

Son: Aye, Ma, this time Ah'm goin' aff.

Mother: Ye might be back in a month or even less. Just wait and see, boy. Far aff fields are green.

Son: Ah might at that. Who's to know what's
           ahead. But sure Ah'll have it to say that
           Ah went away, anyhow, so Ah will.
Mother: Some childer are a bad rarin'.